Peter Sherran and Peter Derych

REVISION PLUS

Edexcel
GCSE Mathematics
for A*

Revision and Classroom Companion

Contents

Rounding Numbers

Rounding a Number to 1 (or more) Decimal Places

To round a number to 1 decimal place (1 d.p.) we must look at the **second** digit after the decimal point. There are two possibilities:

1 If the second digit after the decimal point is **4 or less** (i.e. 0, 1, 2, 3 or 4) we leave the first digit after the decimal point as it is.

2 If the second digit after the decimal point is **5 or more** (i.e. 5, 6, 7, 8 or 9) we **round up** by adding 1 to the first digit after the decimal point.

To round a number to 2 d.p. we are only allowed two digits after the decimal point. This time we must look at the **third** digit after the decimal point to decide whether we need to round the second digit after the decimal point or keep it the same.

To round a number to 3 d.p. we must look at the **fourth** digit and so on. Unless a question tells you otherwise, always give money to 2 decimal places. Amounts of money are rounded to 2 d.p. in exactly the same way as below.

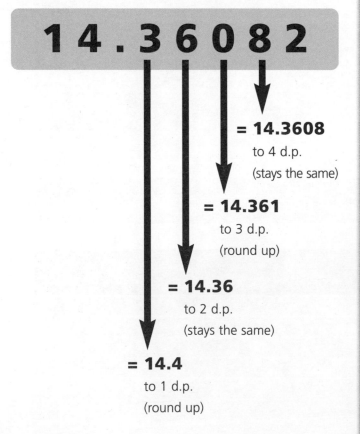

14.36082

= **14.3608**
to 4 d.p.
(stays the same)

= **14.361**
to 3 d.p.
(round up)

= **14.36**
to 2 d.p.
(stays the same)

= **14.4**
to 1 d.p.
(round up)

Rounding a Number to 1 (or more) Significant Figures

Rounding a number to a certain number of significant figures (s.f.) is very like rounding a number to a certain number of decimal places.

The number below shows the attendance at a pop concert. It has 4 significant figures.

1st s.f. 2nd s.f. 3rd s.f. 4th s.f.

6 8 2 5

7000
to 1 s.f.
(round up)

6800
to 2 s.f.
(stays the same)

6830
to 3 s.f.
(round up)

Notice how 0s are used to maintain the place value of the significant figures, e.g. 6825 is 7000 to 1 s.f. not 7.

To round numbers less than 1 we follow the same rules except we start counting our significant figures from the first digit greater than 0 (zero).

1st s.f. 2nd s.f. 3rd s.f. 4th s.f.

0 . 0 3 6 1 7

to 1 s.f. is **0.04**
(round up)

to 2 s.f. is **0.036**
(stays the same)

to 3 s.f. is **0.0362**
(round up)

Decimals

Ordering Decimals

Ordering decimals means rearranging a series of decimals in either ascending (lowest to highest) or descending (highest to lowest) order.

A useful method is to line up all the decimal points of the numbers in a vertical line. Then you can start with the first column on the left, and work along each column of numbers (left to right) to decide which is the highest number.

Example
Rearrange the following in ascending order:
0.54, 5.4, 0.45, 4.5

Line up the decimal points.

Addition and Subtraction of Decimals

When adding and subtracting decimals, you follow the same rules as for whole numbers. The place values of the digits must line up one on top of the other. An easy way is to simply line up your decimal points. Remember to bring the decimal point down to your answer.

Examples

$$
\begin{array}{r}
343.62 \\
+\ \ 17.59 \\
\hline
361.21
\end{array}
$$

$$
\begin{array}{r}
63.184 \\
-\ \ 5.091 \\
\hline
58.093
\end{array}
$$

Recurring and Terminating Decimals

A **terminating decimal** is a decimal that has a finite number of decimal places.

Example
0.5 and 3.142 are terminating decimals.

A **recurring decimal** has an infinite number of decimal places in a repeating pattern.

Example
0.3333... and 0.142857142857... are recurring decimals.
- **0.3333...** may be written as **0.3̇**
  The dot above the 3 indicates that the 3 repeats
- **0.142857142857...** may be written as **0.1̇42857̇**
  Two dots are used here to show the start and the end of the repeating pattern

Converting Recurring Decimals into Fractions

Example
0.2727... the recurring pattern occurs after the second number

Let our recurring decimal be represented by the letter N

$$
\begin{aligned}
N &= 0.2727... \\
100N &= 0.2727... \times 100 \\
100N &= 27.2727...
\end{aligned}
$$

$$
\begin{aligned}
100N - N &= 27.2727... - 0.2727... \\
99N &= 27 \\
N &= \frac{27}{99} = \frac{3}{11}
\end{aligned}
$$

$$
\mathbf{0.2727...} = \frac{3}{11}
$$

Notice that $0.\dot{3} = \frac{1}{3}$. So, $0.\dot{3} \times 3 = \frac{1}{3} \times 3$, i.e. $0.\dot{9} = 1$

Decimals

Multiplication of Decimal Numbers by Whole and Decimal Numbers

To multiply decimals, ignore the decimal points and multiply as you would whole numbers. You put the decimal point back in at the end. In your answer, the number of digits after the decimal point should be the same as the total number of digits after the decimal points in the numbers being multiplied.

Examples

① 2.73×18

```
      2 7 3
  ×     1 8
  2 7 3 0
  2 1⁵8²4
  4 9 1 4
```

Multiply as you would whole numbers

Then, count the digits after the decimal point in the numbers being multiplied and transfer to answer.

$$2.73 \times 18 = 49.14$$

Therefore, $2.73 \times 18 = \mathbf{49.14}$

② 17.5×0.61

```
      1 7 5
  ×     6 1
  1 0⁴5³0 0
      1 7 5
  1 0 6 7 5
```

Multiply as you would whole numbers

Then, count the digits after the decimal point in the numbers being multiplied and transfer to answer.

$$17.5 \times 0.61 = 10.675$$

Therefore $17.5 \times 0.61 = \mathbf{10.675}$

③ Calculate the cost of 6.5m of carpet at £57.34 per metre.

```
      5 7 3 4
  ×       6 5
  3 4 4⁴0²4 0
    2 8 6³7²0
  3 7 2 7 1 0
```

$$57.34 \times 6.5 = 372.710$$

Inserting the decimal point

The carpet costs **= £372.71**

Division of Decimal Numbers by Whole and Decimal Numbers

Division of a decimal number by a whole number is the same as the division of whole numbers. The only exception is that you must remember to take the decimal point up to your answer.

Example

$13.2 \div 6$

```
        2 . 2
  6) 1 3 . 2
      1 2 ↓
        1 2
        1 2
          0
```

Divide as you would whole numbers

Remember to take the decimal point up to the answer

Therefore, $13.2 \div 6 = \mathbf{2.2}$

Division of a decimal number by another decimal number is slightly more tricky. Before you start, multiply both numbers by 10, 100, etc. until the number doing the dividing is a whole number. The process from now on is the same as the example above.

Example

$4.368 \div 0.56$

Multiply both numbers by 100 to make the divisor a whole number. **4.368 × 100 = 436.8, 0.56 × 100 = 56**

Divide as you would whole numbers.

```
          7 . 8
  56) 4 3 6 . 8
      3 9 2 ↓
        4 4   8
        4 4   8
              0
```

Remember to take the decimal point up to the answer

Therefore $4.368 \div 0.56 = \mathbf{7.8}$

Notice that 7.8 > 4.368, which shows that division by 0.56 has had an increasing effect. This happens because $0 < 0.56 < 1$

Types of Number

Numbers can be described in many ways. Below is a summary of the types of number that you should know.

Even Numbers

Even numbers are numbers that can be divided exactly by 2. The first ten even numbers in order are…

2, 4, 6, 8, 10, 12, 14, 16, 18, 20

Odd Numbers

Since all whole numbers are either even or odd, then odd numbers are those that cannot be divided exactly by 2.

The first ten odd numbers in order are…

1, 3, 5, 7, 9, 11, 13, 15, 17, 19

Factors (Divisors)

The factors (or divisors) of a number are those whole numbers that divide exactly into it. All numbers, with the exception of square numbers (see page 9), have an even number of factors.

An easy way to find the factors of a number is to choose pairs of numbers that multiply to give that number.

Examples

The factors of **10** are **1, 2, 5, 10**

(since 1 x 10 = 10, 2 x 5 = 10)

The factors of **24** are **1, 2, 3, 4, 6, 8, 12, 24**

(since 1 x 24 = 24, 2 x 12 = 24, 3 x 8 = 24, 4 x 6 = 24)

Square numbers have an odd number of factors.

Examples

The factors of **16** are **1, 2, 4, 8, 16**

(since 1 x 16 = 16, 2 x 8 = 16, 4 x 4 = 16)

The factors of **36** are **1, 2, 3, 4, 6, 9, 12, 18, 36**

(since 1 x 36 = 36, 2 x 18 = 36, 3 x 12 = 36, 4 x 9 = 36, 6 x 6 = 36)

Multiples

The multiples of a number are those numbers that can be divided exactly by it. To put it simply, they are the numbers found in the 'times' tables.

- The multiples of **5** are **5, 10, 15, 20, 25**, etc.
- The multiples of **8** are **8, 16, 24, 32, 40**, etc.

Prime Numbers

Prime numbers are numbers that have only two factors: 1 and the number itself. The first ten prime numbers are…

2, 3, 5, 7, 11, 13, 17, 19, 23, 29

The only even prime number is 2 since all even numbers after this have 2 as a factor, which rules them out as prime numbers.

Reciprocals

The reciprocal of a number is '1 over that number'.

Examples

1. The reciprocal of 4 is '1 over 4' $= \frac{1}{4}$

2. The reciprocal of 0.2 is '1 over 0.2'

$$= \frac{1}{0.2} \overset{\times 10}{\underset{\times 10}{=}} \frac{10}{2} = 5$$

3. The reciprocal of $\frac{2}{3}$ is '1 over $\frac{2}{3}$'

$$= \frac{1}{\frac{2}{3}} = 1 \div \frac{2}{3} = 1 \times \frac{3}{2} = \frac{3}{2} = 1\frac{1}{2}$$

Any number (apart from zero) multiplied by its reciprocal is equal to 1.

Examples

1. $4 \times \frac{1}{4} = 1$

2. $0.2 \times 5 = 1$

3. $\frac{2}{3} \times \frac{3}{2} = 1$

Zero has no reciprocal because anything divided by zero is undefined.

Number Properties

Prime Factor Form

The prime factors of a number are those prime numbers that divide exactly into it. When a number is expressed as a product of its prime factors it is said to be written in prime factor form. To find the prime factor form, try to divide your number by the lowest prime number (i.e. 2). If it works, keep repeating until it will not divide exactly. Then try the next prime number up, and continue until you have an answer of 1. This process is called **prime number decomposition**.

Examples

① Write **24** in prime factor form.

$$
\begin{array}{c|c}
2 & 24 \\
2 & 12 \\
2 & 6 \\
3 & 3 \\
& 1
\end{array}
$$

so **24 = 2 × 2 × 2 × 3 = 2^3 × 3**

② Write **420** in prime factor form.

$$
\begin{array}{c|c}
2 & 420 \\
2 & 210 \\
3 & 105 \\
5 & 35 \\
7 & 7 \\
& 1
\end{array}
$$

so **420 = 2 × 2 × 3 × 5 × 7 = 2^2 × 3 × 5 × 7**

Alternatively, a prime factor tree can be used to work out the prime factors of a number.

Example

Pick two numbers that when multiplied together give 24

Repeat for 4 and 6

2 × 2 × 2 × 3 or **2^3 × 3** is the prime factor form of 24.

Highest Common Factor

The highest common factor (HCF) of two (or more) numbers is the highest number that divides exactly into both (or all of) the numbers. To find the HCF, express your numbers in prime factor form and then select only the prime factors that are common to both numbers.

Example
What is the HCF of **24** and **90**?

First express **24** and **90** in prime factor form

24 = 2 × 2 × ⎡2 × 3⎤
90 =   ⎣2 × 3⎦ × 3 × 5

Then select prime factors that are common to both numbers.

HCF of 24 and 90 = 2 × 3 = 6

Lowest (Least) Common Multiple

The lowest (least) common multiple (LCM) of two or more numbers is the lowest number that is a multiple of all the numbers. You can use prime number decomposition to find the LCM.

Example
What is the LCM of **8** and **10**?

Write the two numbers down in prime factor form

$$
\begin{array}{c|c}
2 & 8 \\
2 & 4 \\
2 & 2 \\
& 1
\end{array}
\qquad
\begin{array}{c|c}
2 & 10 \\
5 & 5 \\
& 1
\end{array}
$$

so **8 = 2 × 2 × 2 = 2^3**   so **10 = 2 × 5**

Then select the highest power of each prime factor that appears and form a single multiplication.

LCM of 8 and 10 is 2^3 × 5 = 40

Powers

Understanding Powers

Powers or indices show that a number is to be multiplied by itself a certain number of times.

$$4 \times 4 = 4^2 \text{ (4 squared)}$$
$$4 \times 4 \times 4 = 4^3 \text{ (4 cubed)}$$
$$4 \times 4 \times 4 \times 4 = 4^4 \text{ (4 to the power 4)}$$
$$4 \times 4 \times 4 \times 4 \times 4 = 4^5 \text{ (4 to the power 5)}$$

… and so on

4^2 ← The power or index

Powers of Negative Numbers

Care is needed when working out powers of negative numbers.

Examples

1 $(-4)^2 = -4 \times -4 = \mathbf{16}$ ← A 'minus' times a 'minus' is equal to a 'plus'

2 $(-4)^3 = -4 \times -4 \times -4 = \mathbf{-64}$ ← The first two 'minuses' give a 'plus'. This 'plus' times a 'minus' then gives a 'minus'

3 $(-1)^{99} = \mathbf{-1}$ ← 99 is an odd power

4 $\left(\frac{1}{2}\right)^2 = \frac{1}{4}, \ \left(\frac{1}{2}\right)^3 = \frac{1}{8}$

$\therefore \ \left(\frac{1}{2}\right)^3 < \left(\frac{1}{2}\right)^2$ ← Raising the power reduces the value

Square Numbers

Numbers obtained by squaring whole numbers (integers) are called square numbers, for example…

4 squared $= 4^2 = 4 \times 4 = 16$
9 squared $= 9^2 = 9 \times 9 = 81$

The first four square numbers are…

1 $(1^2 = 1 \times 1)$ **4** $(2^2 = 2 \times 2)$ **9** $(3^2 = 3 \times 3)$ **16** $(4^2 = 4 \times 4)$

You are expected to be able to recall integer squares from 2^2 to 15^2.

$2^2=$	$3^2=$	$4^2=$	$5^2=$	$6^2=$	$7^2=$	$8^2=$
4	9	16	25	36	49	64

$9^2=$	$10^2=$	$11^2=$	$12^2=$	$13^2=$	$14^2=$	$15^2=$
81	100	121	144	169	196	225

Cube Numbers

Numbers obtained by cubing whole numbers are called cube numbers, for example…

4 cubed $= 4^3 = 4 \times 4 \times 4 = 64$
9 cubed $= 9^3 = 9 \times 9 \times 9 = 729$

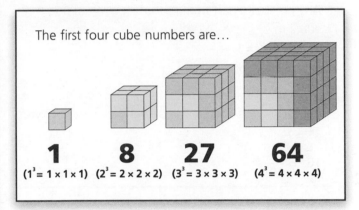

The first four cube numbers are…

1 $(1^3 = 1 \times 1 \times 1)$ **8** $(2^3 = 2 \times 2 \times 2)$ **27** $(3^3 = 3 \times 3 \times 3)$ **64** $(4^3 = 4 \times 4 \times 4)$

You are expected to be able to recall the cubes of the following numbers:

$2^3=$	$3^3=$	$4^3=$	$5^3=$	$10^3=$
8	27	64	125	1000

Powers in Formulae

Many mathematical formulae include the use of powers, e.g. $V = \pi r^2 h$ for the volume of a cylinder.

Example
Calculate the capacity of a pipe of internal radius 1.4m and length 30m to 1 d.p.

$V = \pi r^2 h$
$\quad = \pi \times 1.4^2 \times 30$
$\quad = 184.725...\text{m}^3$
$\quad = \mathbf{184.7 m^3}$

Powers

Rules of Indices

① A number to a power of 1 is the number itself.

$3^1 = 3$

$10^1 = 10$

② To multiply powers of the same number, we add the indices.

$3^5 \times 3^2 = 3^{5+2} = 3^7$, $10^3 \times 10 = 10^{3+1} = 10^4$

③ To divide powers of the same number, we subtract the indices.

$3^5 \div 3^2 = 3^{5-2} = 3^3$, $10^3 \div 10 = 10^{3-1} = 10^2$

④ To raise the power of a number to another power, we multiply the indices.

$(3^5)^2 = 3^{5 \times 2} = 3^{10}$, $(10^3)^1 = 10^{3 \times 1} = 10^3$

⑤ Any number (apart from 0) to the power of 0 is equal to 1

$3^0 = 1$, $10^0 = 1$

Note that 0^0 is undefined.

⑥ A number to a negative power is one over that number to the power. The power becomes positive.

$3^{-2} = \dfrac{1}{3^2}$

$10^{-1} = \dfrac{1}{10^1}$

Examples

① Evaluate $\dfrac{3^4 \times 3^7}{3^8}$

$= \dfrac{3^{4+7}}{3^8}$ — Do the multiplication first. Then the division

$= 3^{11-8}$

$= 3^3$

$= 27$

② Evaluate $\dfrac{(2^4)^2}{2^{-5}}$

$= \dfrac{2^{4 \times 2}}{2^{-5}}$ — Do the power raised to another power first. Then the division

$= 2^{8--5}$

$= 2^{8+5}$ — The same rules still apply for negative powers as for positive powers

$= 2^{13}$

③ Evaluate $\dfrac{4^7 \times 4^{-2}}{4^5}$

$= \dfrac{4^{7+-2}}{4^5}$ — Do the multiplication first. Then the division

$= 4^{5-5}$

$= 4^0$

$= 1$

Fractional Powers

A fractional power simply means a square root, cube root, etc. (See page 11).

① $4^{\frac{1}{2}}$ means $\sqrt{4} = 2$ — A power of $\frac{1}{2}$ means square root

② $27^{\frac{1}{3}}$ means $\sqrt[3]{27} = 3$ — A power of $\frac{1}{3}$ means square root

③ $10\,000^{\frac{1}{4}}$ means $\sqrt[4]{10\,000} = 10$ — A power of $\frac{1}{4}$ means fourth root

The inverse (opposite) operation of raising a positive number to power 'n' is raising the result of this operation to power '$\frac{1}{n}$', for example...

$4^2 = 16$ and $16^{\frac{1}{2}} = 4$

$5^3 = 125$ and $125^{\frac{1}{3}} = 5$

Examples

① Calculate $8^{\frac{2}{3}}$

In this case we need to split the fractional power up into two powers, i.e. $\frac{2}{3} = \frac{1}{3} \times 2$. We can now do the calculation in two stages.

Therefore...

$8^{\frac{2}{3}} = 8^{\frac{1}{3} \times 2} = 2^2 = 4$

stage 1 — stage 2

Cube root Square
of 8 = 2 of 2 = 4

Always do the root first (as this decreases the size of your number), and then the power

② Calculate $32^{\frac{3}{5}}$

$32^{\frac{3}{5}} = 32^{\frac{1}{5} \times 3} = 2^3 = 8$

stage 1 — stage 2

Fifth root Cube of
of 32 = 2 2 = 8

A* Tip

You need to understand the meaning of fractional and negative powers.

Roots

Square Roots of Positive Numbers

Every positive number has two square roots, for example…

$$4^2 = 16$$
$$(-4)^2 = 16$$

…therefore, 4 and -4 are both square roots of 16.

If $x^2 = 16$ then $x = \pm\sqrt{16} = \pm 4$

The symbol $\sqrt{}$ is only used to represent **positive** square roots.

Since $a^2 > 0$ for any value of a, it follows that we can only find the square roots of positive numbers.

You will be expected to be able to recall the square roots of all integer squares from 2^2 (4) to 15^2 (225).

$\sqrt{4}=$	$\sqrt{9}=$	$\sqrt{16}=$	$\sqrt{25}=$	$\sqrt{36}=$	$\sqrt{49}=$	$\sqrt{64}=$
2	3	4	5	6	7	8

$\sqrt{81}=$	$\sqrt{100}=$	$\sqrt{121}=$	$\sqrt{144}=$	$\sqrt{169}=$	$\sqrt{196}=$	$\sqrt{225}=$
9	10	11	12	13	14	15

Cube Roots of Positive Numbers

Finding the cube root of a positive number results in only one root – a positive root.

Since $4^3 = 4 \times 4 \times 4 = 64$, then **4 is the cube root of 64**.

Therefore, $\sqrt[3]{64}$ or $64^{\frac{1}{3}} = 4$

Similarly…

$\sqrt[3]{125}$ or $125^{\frac{1}{3}} = 5$ (since $5 \times 5 \times 5 = 125$)

$\sqrt[3]{1000}$ or $1000^{\frac{1}{3}} = 10$ (since $10 \times 10 \times 10 = 1000$)

Cube Roots of Negative Numbers

Since $-4 \times -4 \times -4 = -64$, it follows that $\sqrt[3]{(-64)} = -4$

Similarly $\sqrt[3]{(-125)} = -5$

Surds

Some numbers (square numbers) have an exact square root, e.g. $\sqrt{4} = 2$. Other numbers do not, e.g. $\sqrt{5} = 2.236067$. Since $\sqrt{5}$ cannot be written as an exact number, it is more accurate to leave it as $\sqrt{5}$. When it is written in this form, $\sqrt{5}$ is called a surd. Many surds can be simplified.

Examples

1. $\sqrt{18} = \sqrt{9 \times 2} = \sqrt{9} \times \sqrt{2} = 3 \times \sqrt{2} = \mathbf{3\sqrt{2}}$
2. $\sqrt{48} = \sqrt{16 \times 3} = \sqrt{16} \times \sqrt{3} = 4 \times \sqrt{3} = \mathbf{4\sqrt{3}}$
3. $\dfrac{\sqrt{10}}{\sqrt{2}} = \sqrt{\dfrac{10}{2}} = \mathbf{\sqrt{5}}$
4. In general, $(a - b)^2 = a^2 - 2ab + b^2$

   So, $(4 - \sqrt{3})^2 = 4^2 - 2 \times 4\sqrt{3} + (\sqrt{3})^2$
   $$= 16 - 8\sqrt{3} + 3$$
   $$= \mathbf{19 - 8\sqrt{3}}$$
5. In general, $(a + b)(a - b) = a^2 - b^2$

   So, $(3 + \sqrt{5})(3 - \sqrt{5}) = 3^2 - (\sqrt{5})^2$
   $$= \mathbf{9 - 5 = 4}$$

Decimal numbers that are neither terminating nor recurring (see page 5) are known as irrational numbers. All other numbers are rational. For example, the square root of 5 is 2.236067… (i.e. a decimal number that does not terminate or recur.) This is an example of an irrational number.

The following example shows you how to rationalise a denominator.

$$\frac{2}{\sqrt{5}} = \frac{2 \times \sqrt{5}}{\sqrt{5} \times \sqrt{5}} = \frac{2\sqrt{5}}{5}$$

> Multiply the numerator (top number) and denominator (bottom number) by the denominator itself, e.g. $\sqrt{5}$.

The denominator is now a rational number.

Sometimes we need to make use of the algebraic result $(a + b)(a - b) = a^2 - b^2$ to rationalise a denominator.

Example
Rationalise $\dfrac{8}{3 - \sqrt{5}}$

$$\frac{8}{3 - \sqrt{5}} = \frac{8}{3 - \sqrt{5}} \times \frac{3 + \sqrt{5}}{3 + \sqrt{5}}$$

$$= \frac{8(3 + \sqrt{5})}{3^2 - 5} = \frac{8(3 + \sqrt{5})}{4} = \mathbf{2(3 + \sqrt{5})}$$

A* Tip

With square roots, make it clear what goes under the horizontal part of the sign, i.e. the line needs to go all the way across. When there is a fraction, ensure that the downward part of the square root sign goes to the foot of the denominator if both parts are included.

Order of Operations

BIDMAS

The simplest possible calculation involves only one operation, e.g. an addition or multiplication.

However, when a calculation involves more than one operation, you must carry them out in the order shown here.

BIDMAS

| Brackets | Indices (or powers) | Divisions and Multiplications – these can be done in any order | Additions and Subtractions – these can be done in any order |

Examples

1 $8 + 3 \times 4$ ← Do the multiplication first

$= 8 + 12$ ← Then the addition

$= 20$

2 $\dfrac{(14 + 6)}{-4}$ ← Do the addition in the bracket first

$= \dfrac{20}{-4}$ ← Then the division (+ ÷ - = -)

$= -5$

3 $4^2 - 2 \times 5$ ← Work out the square first

$= 16 - 2 \times 5$ ← Then the multiplication

$= 16 - 10$ ← Then the subtraction

$= 6$

4 4×3^2 ← Work out the square first. A common mistake is to work out 12^2, which is 144

$= 4 \times 9$ ← Then the multiplication

$= 36$

Use of Brackets

Inserting brackets into a calculation changes the order in which the operations are carried out and this produces different answers.

Examples

1 Here is a calculation without brackets.

$8 + 3 \times 4 - 2 = 8 + 12 - 2 = 20 - 2 = 18$
(or 8 + 10)

If we now insert one pair of brackets into the calculation we can obtain…

$(8 + 3) \times 4 - 2 = 11 \times 4 - 2 = 44 - 2 = 42$
$8 + 3 \times (4 - 2) = 8 + 3 \times 2 = 8 + 6 = 14$

2 The diagram represents part of a garden that is to be paved. The cost of the paving is £15 per m². Calculate the total cost.

Area = $(25 \times 14 - 12 \times 6) = 278\text{m}^2$
Cost = $278 \times 15 =$ **£4170**

A* Tip

When the question is set in a context, make sure your answer is in the same context. For example, if a question involves money, the answer 7.3 will not get full marks – it should be £7.30.

Standard Index Form

What is Standard Index Form?

Standard index form is a way of writing numbers that makes it easier to deal with very large and very small numbers.

A number written as $a \times 10^n$, where $1 \leqslant a < 10$ and n is an integer, is said to be written in standard index form.

For **large** numbers, n is a **positive integer** and is equal to the number of places the decimal point has moved.

Examples

1. $4372 = \mathbf{4.372 \times 10^3}$ The decimal point has moved 3 places

2. $691\,000 = \mathbf{6.91 \times 10^5}$ The decimal point has moved 5 places

3. $3.71 \times 10^4 = \mathbf{37100}$ Numbers written in standard index form can also be converted to ordinary numbers

For **small** positive numbers, n is a **negative integer** (**min**us for **min**ute numbers) and is equal to the number of places the decimal point has moved.

Examples

1. $0.0356 = \mathbf{3.56 \times 10^{-2}}$ The decimal point has moved 2 places

2. $0.000\,13 = \mathbf{1.3 \times 10^{-4}}$ The decimal point has moved 4 places

3. $4.5712 \times 10^{-5} = \mathbf{0.000\,045\,712}$ Numbers written in standard index form can also be converted to ordinary numbers

Calculations with Standard Index Form

To add or subtract numbers written in standard index form, convert to 'ordinary numbers', do the calculation and then, if required, change your answer back into standard index form.

To multiply or divide numbers written in standard index form, carry out separate calculations for the numbers and powers and then rearrange your answer back into standard index form.

Examples

1. $4.2 \times 10^4 + 8.6 \times 10^3$
   $= 42000 + 8600$
   $= 50600$
   $= \mathbf{5.06 \times 10^4}$

2. $9.37 \times 10^{-2} - 1.6 \times 10^{-3}$
   $= 0.0937 - 0.0016$
   $= 0.0921$
   $= \mathbf{9.21 \times 10^{-2}}$

3. $3.2 \times 10^{-3} \times 4.5 \times 10^{-4}$
   $= (3.2 \times 4.5) \times (10^{-3} \times 10^{-4})$
   $= 14.4 \times 10^{-7}$
   $= \mathbf{1.44 \times 10^1 \times 10^{-7} = 1.44 \times 10^{-6}}$

4. $5.6 \times 10^5 \div 8 \times 10^1$
   $= (5.6 \div 8) \times (10^5 \div 10^1)$
   $= 0.7 \times 10^4$
   $= \mathbf{7 \times 10^{-1} \times 10^4 = 7 \times 10^3}$

5.   Light travels at $186\,000$ miles per second. A light year is the distance that light will travel in one year. The number of miles in a light year is given by…
   $186000 \times 60 \times 60 \times 24 \times 365$
   Complete this calculation and give your answer in standard form.
   $= \mathbf{5.87 \times 10^{12}}$ The answer is too large to be displayed as an ordinary number on a calculator. It is automatically given in standard form.

Ordering Numbers in Standard Index Form

To order numbers in standard index form, first look at the value of n. The largest numbers have the highest powers of 10. For numbers with the same value of n, compare the values of a.

Example

Write these numbers in descending order
7.8×10^5, 3.2×10^8, 6.5×10^5.

The number with the largest value of n is 3.2×10^8. The other two numbers have the same value of n but $7.8 > 6.5$

So, the numbers are…
$\mathbf{3.2 \times 10^8}$, $\mathbf{7.8 \times 10^5}$, $\mathbf{6.5 \times 10^5}$

Fractions

Understanding Simple Fractions

The diagram shows a whole pizza that has been cut into four equal parts (or slices). Each slice can be described as a fraction of the whole pizza and its value is $\frac{1}{4}$.

$\frac{1}{4}$

The pizza, however, could have been cut into any number of slices, where each slice is a different fraction of the whole pizza (see the diagrams below).

The top number of a fraction is called the **numerator**, while the bottom number is called the **denominator**.

$\frac{1}{2}$ $\frac{1}{3}$ $\frac{2}{3}$

$\frac{1}{4}$ $\frac{1}{5}$ $\frac{4}{5}$

$\frac{1}{6}$

Equivalent Fractions

Equivalent fractions are fractions that are equal. You can build chains of equivalent fractions by multiplying the numerator and denominator in the fraction by the same number.

$$\frac{1}{4} \overset{\times 2}{\underset{\times 2}{=}} \frac{2}{8} \overset{\times 3}{\underset{\times 3}{=}} \frac{6}{24} \overset{\times 4}{\underset{\times 4}{=}} \frac{24}{96}$$

Cancelling Fractions

You can also divide the numerator and denominator in a fraction by the same number. Chains of equivalent fractions that are cancelled down using division always come to an end when the fraction is expressed in its simplest form, i.e. lowest terms.

$$\frac{18}{27} \overset{\div 3}{\underset{\div 3}{=}} \frac{6}{9} \overset{\div 3}{\underset{\div 3}{=}} \frac{2}{3} \quad \text{or} \quad \frac{18}{27} \overset{\div 9}{\underset{\div 9}{=}} \frac{2}{3}$$

Ordering Fractions

To put fractions in order, first we need to write each fraction with a common denominator.

> **Example**
> Arrange $\frac{9}{10}, \frac{4}{5}, \frac{7}{8}$ in ascending order.
>
> The lowest common multiple of 10, 5 and 8 is 40.
>
> $$\frac{9}{10} \overset{\times 4}{\underset{\times 4}{=}} \frac{36}{40} \quad \frac{4}{5} \overset{\times 8}{\underset{\times 8}{=}} \frac{32}{40} \quad \frac{7}{8} \overset{\times 5}{\underset{\times 5}{=}} \frac{35}{40}$$
>
> If we now compare the numerators we can arrange the fractions in ascending (lowest to highest) order.
>
> In ascending order they are: $\frac{4}{5}, \frac{7}{8}, \frac{9}{10}$.

When you have fractions with common denominators, it is possible to find other fractions that lie between them.

For example, as seen above $\frac{4}{5} = \frac{32}{40}$ and $\frac{7}{8} = \frac{35}{40}$. We can write two other fractions with denominator 40 that are greater than $\frac{4}{5}$ but less than $\frac{7}{8}$. They would be $\frac{33}{40}$ and $\frac{34}{40}$, which cancels down to $\frac{17}{20}$.

Calculations with Fractions

Addition of Fractions

Two fractions can be added very easily providing they have a common denominator.

Example

$\frac{2}{5} = \frac{8}{20}$ $\quad \frac{2}{5} + \frac{3}{4}$ $\quad \frac{3}{4} = \frac{15}{20}$

$= \frac{8}{20} + \frac{15}{20}$

$= \frac{23}{20}$

$= 1\frac{3}{20}$

With mixed numbers, add the whole numbers and fractions separately and then combine.

Example

$2\frac{2}{3} + 3\frac{1}{7}$

$= (2 + 3) + (\frac{2}{3} + \frac{1}{7})$

$= 5 + (\frac{14}{21} + \frac{3}{21})$

$= 5\frac{17}{21}$

Subtraction of Fractions

As with addition, two fractions can be subtracted very easily providing they have common denominators.

Example

$\frac{7}{8} = \frac{21}{24}$ $\quad \frac{7}{8} - \frac{2}{3}$ $\quad \frac{2}{3} = \frac{16}{24}$

$= \frac{21}{24} - \frac{16}{24}$

$= \frac{5}{24}$

With mixed numbers, subtract the whole numbers and fractions separately and then combine.

Example

$4\frac{1}{2} - 1\frac{4}{5}$

$= (4 - 1) + (\frac{1}{2} - \frac{4}{5})$

$= 3 + (\frac{5}{10} - \frac{8}{10})$

$= 3 + (-\frac{3}{10})$

$= 3 - \frac{3}{10}$

$= 2\frac{7}{10}$

Alternatively, you can use improper fractions.

$4\frac{1}{2} - 1\frac{4}{5}$

$= \frac{9}{2} - \frac{9}{5}$

$= \frac{45}{10} - \frac{18}{10}$

$= \frac{27}{10}$

$= 2\frac{7}{10}$

Multiplication and Division of Fractions

To multiply two fractions, multiply the two numerators together and multiply the two denominators together.

Example $\quad \frac{2}{3} \times \frac{4}{5} = \frac{2\times4}{3\times5} = \frac{8}{15}$

Division of two fractions is the same as multiplication, except that you turn the second fraction (that is doing the dividing) upside down and change the division sign to a multiplication sign.

Example $\quad \frac{2}{3} \div \frac{4}{5} = \frac{2}{3} \times \frac{5}{4} = \frac{2\times5}{3\times4} = \frac{10}{12} = \frac{5}{6}$

To multiply or divide mixed numbers you have to convert them to improper fractions first.

Examples

① $2\frac{1}{2} \times 1\frac{1}{6} = \frac{5}{2} \times \frac{7}{6}$

$= \frac{5\times7}{2\times6}$

$= \frac{35}{12}$

$= 2\frac{11}{12}$

② $1\frac{1}{3} \div 3\frac{1}{2} = \frac{4}{3} \div \frac{7}{2}$

$= \frac{4}{3} \times \frac{2}{7}$

$= \frac{4\times2}{3\times7}$

$= \frac{8}{21}$

To multiply or divide a fraction by an integer, convert the integer to an improper fraction. For example, 4 as an improper fraction is $\frac{4}{1}$. You can then do the multiplication or division as normal.

Examples

① $\frac{2}{3} \div 10 = \frac{2}{3} \div \frac{10}{1}$

$= \frac{2}{3} \times \frac{1}{10}$

$= \frac{2\times1}{3\times10}$

$= \frac{2}{30}$

$= \frac{1}{15}$

② $1\frac{4}{7} \times 3 = \frac{11}{7} \times \frac{3}{1}$

$= \frac{11\times3}{7\times1}$

$= \frac{33}{7}$

$= 4\frac{5}{7}$

Calculations with Fractions

Calculating a Fraction of a Quantity

To find a fraction of any quantity, you have to multiply the fraction by the quantity. In other words, 'of' means 'times' or 'multiply' (×).

Examples

1. Calculate $\frac{4}{5}$ of 60kg.

$$\frac{4}{5} \text{ of } 60\text{kg} = \frac{4}{5} \times 60 \quad \boxed{\text{'of' means '×'}}$$

$$= \frac{4}{5} \times \frac{60}{1} = \frac{240}{5} = \textbf{48kg}$$

Alternatively: $\frac{4}{\cancel{5}_1} \times \frac{\cancel{60}^{12}}{1} = \frac{48}{1} = \textbf{48kg}$

2. A brand new car costing £9000 will lose $\frac{1}{5}$ of its value in the first year. What is the value of the car after the first year?

Before we can calculate its value we need to calculate the loss.

$$\text{Loss} = \frac{1}{5} \text{ of } £9000 = \frac{1}{5} \times 9000$$

$$\boxed{\text{'of' means '×'}}$$

$$= \frac{9000}{5} = £1800$$

Value of car after the first year

$$= £9000 - £1800 = \textbf{£7200}$$

OR $1 - \frac{1}{5} = \frac{4}{5}$ of value after first year
$$= £9000 \times \frac{4}{5} = \frac{36\,000}{5} = \textbf{£7200}$$

3. A marathon runner covers a distance of $12\frac{1}{2}$ miles in $1\frac{1}{4}$ hours on a training run. What is his average speed?

$$\boxed{\textbf{Average speed} = \frac{\textbf{Distance}}{\textbf{Time}}}$$

$$= 12\frac{1}{2} \div 1\frac{1}{4}$$

$$= \frac{25}{2} \div \frac{5}{4}$$

$$= \frac{\cancel{25}^5}{\cancel{2}_1} \times \frac{\cancel{4}^2}{\cancel{5}_1}$$

$$= \frac{10}{1}$$

$$= \textbf{10 miles per hour}$$

Expressing One Quantity as a Fraction of Another Quantity

To express one quantity as a fraction of another quantity, first you must make sure that both quantities are in the same units. Then, to express the relationship as a fraction, the first quantity becomes the numerator and the second quantity becomes the denominator. If need be, write the fraction in its lowest terms.

Examples

1. Write 30 out of 120 as a fraction.

$$30 \text{ out of } 120 = \frac{30}{120} = \frac{1}{4}$$

2. Express 36 seconds as a fraction of 2 minutes.

Both quantities must be in the same units, so change 2 minutes into seconds.

2 minutes = 2 × 60s = 120s, so…

$$36\text{s as a fraction of } 120\text{s} = \frac{36}{120} = \frac{3}{10}$$

Percentages

Understanding Simple Percentages

Percentages are used in everyday life, from pay rises to price reductions. Percentages help us to make easy comparisons.

Percentages focus on the whole being equal to one hundred, i.e. the whole is one hundred percent. So, if someone gives you 50% of a whole pizza this tells you the 'number of parts per 100' you have, e.g. 50% is 50 parts per 100 or $\frac{50}{100}$.

100%

10%   **30%**   **50%**

20%   **40%**

Calculating a Percentage of a Quantity

Example

Calculate 15% of £4.80. Give your answer in pence.

£4.80 = 4.80 × 100p = 480p

15% means 15 parts out of 100 or $\frac{15}{100}$ and 'of' means 'times' (×)

15% of 480p = $\frac{15}{100} \times 480 = \frac{\overset{3}{15} \times \overset{24}{480}}{\underset{\underset{1}{20}}{100}}$

$= \frac{72}{1} = \textbf{72p}$

Expressing One Quantity as a Percentage of Another Quantity

When expressing one quantity as a percentage of another quantity, make sure that both quantities are in the same units. Firstly, express one quantity as a fraction of the other, where the first quantity becomes the numerator and the second quantity becomes the denominator. Then multiply the fraction by 100%.

Example

Express 30cm as a percentage of 3m.

Both quantities must be in the same units, so change 3m into centimetres.

3m = 3 × 100cm = 300cm, so…

30cm as a percentage of 300cm = $\frac{30}{300} \times 100\%$

$= \frac{\overset{1}{30} \times 100}{\underset{10}{300}} = \textbf{10\%}$

Finding Percentage Profit / Loss

Percentage profit and loss are calculated by the following formulae.

$$\text{Percentage profit} = \frac{\text{Actual profit}}{\text{Original price}} \times 100\%$$

$$\text{Percentage loss} = \frac{\text{Actual loss}}{\text{Original price}} \times 100\%$$

Examples

1 A radio is bought for £16 and sold for £20. What is the percentage profit?

Actual profit = £4

∴ Percentage profit $\frac{4}{16} \times 100 = \textbf{25\%}$

2 A car is sold new for £12 000. After 3 years it has depreciated in value to £7200. What is the percentage difference in value of the car?

Actual loss = £4800

Percentage loss = $\frac{4800}{12000} \times 100 = \textbf{40\%}$

Percentage Change

Calculations Involving Comparisons

Calculations involving comparisons are calculations where the original amount has been increased or decreased by a certain percentage. You must remember that the original amount is always equal to 100% and that the transformed amount will always be a percentage that is above or below 100%.

Examples

1 A standard box of breakfast cereal weighs 500g. Special boxes contain an extra 25%. Calculate the weight of a special box of cereal.

> Firstly calculate the increase in weight

$$25\% \text{ of } 500g = \frac{25}{100} \times 500g$$

$$= \frac{\overset{1}{25} \times \overset{125}{500}}{\underset{1}{100}} = \textbf{125g}$$

> Then add it to the weight of a standard box of cereal

Weight of special box = 500g + 125g = **625g**

> An alternative method would be as follows: A standard box of cereal is to be increased by 25%. If a standard box is 100%, a special box will be 100% + 25% = 125%.
>
> $125\% = \frac{125}{100} = \textbf{1.25}$
>
> In other words, the weight of a special box is 1.25 times the weight of a standard box.
>
> $500 \times 1.25 = \textbf{625g}$

2 On 1st January John's weight is 80kg. In the first six months of the year his weight increases by 8%, followed by a 8% decrease in the second six months of the year. What is his weight at the end of the year (to 2 d.p.)?

After the first six months, his weight is 100% + 8% = 108% of his original weight.

$$108\% = \frac{108}{100} = \textbf{1.08}$$

i.e. his weight is now 1.08 times his original amount.

After the second six months, his weight is 100% – 8% = 92% of his weight at the end of the first six months.

$$92\% = \frac{92}{100} = \textbf{0.92}$$

i.e. his weight becomes 0.92 times the previous amount, which is actually a decrease.

Weight at the end of the year =
80 × 1.08 × 0.92 = **79.49kg**

3 A bouncing ball is dropped from a height of 5m. It reaches 80% of its previous height after every bounce. How high does it reach after the third bounce?

$$80\% = \frac{80}{100} = \textbf{0.8}$$

So, the height the ball reaches is 0.8 times the previous height reached.

After three bounces, height reached
= 5m × 0.8 × 0.8 × 0.8 = **2.56m**

> This is an example of a repeated multiplier:
> $0.8 \times 0.8 \times 0.8 = 0.8^3$ (0.8 to the power 3).
> So, you could simply write…
>
> **After three bounces, height reached**
> = $5 \times 0.8^3 = 5 \times 0.512 = \textbf{2.56m}$

Interest

Simple interest is paid **per annum** and is the same amount each year.

Compound interest is where interest is paid on any interest earned as well as on the original sum.

Examples

1. Katie has £3000 in her savings account. Compound interest is paid at 3.9% pa. How much will she have in her account after 3 years?

   Year 1: $1.039 \times 3000 = £3117$

   Year 2: $1.039 \times 3117 = £3238.563$

   Year 3: $1.039 \times 3238.56 = £3364.866$

   Total = £3364.87

   Alternatively you can calculate using a method multiplier.

   $\frac{103.9}{100} = 1.039$ **(this is the multiplier)**

   $= 3000 \times (1.039)^3$

   $= 3364.87$

2. Mrs Johnson's salary is £30 000 per year. Every year her salary is increased by 5%.

   a) What will her salary be in 4 years time?

   $30\,000 \times (1.05)^4 = £36\,465.19$

   b) What will her salary be in 6 years time?

   $30\,000 \times (1.05)^6 = £40\,202.87$

Examples

4. A shop offers 10% off all its clothes. A shirt has a sale price of £27. What was the original price of the shirt?

   Original price of shirt = 100%
   Sale price of shirt = 100% − 10%
   = 90%
   The sale price is 90% of the original price.

   ×0.9
   Original price ⟷ **Sale price**
   ÷0.9

   Original price of the shirt = $\frac{27}{0.9}$ = **£30**

5. A company allocates £15 000 of its budget to be spent on advertising. This is a 20% increase on the money budgeted for advertising last year. How much money did the company budget for advertising last year?

   The original amount in this question is the money budgeted for advertising last year.

   ×1.2
   Last year's budget ⟷ **This year's budget**
   ÷1.2

   Last year's budget = $\frac{£15\,000}{1.2}$ = **£12 500**

Ratios

What is a Ratio?

A ratio is a comparison between two or more quantities; it has no units. The image shows two columns of coins. The first column has ten £1 coins and the second column has six 2p coins. To compare the two sets of coins we can say that the ratio of the number of £1 coins to 2p coins is…

10 to 6 or 10 : 6

Ratios can be simplified into their simplest form, just like fractions…

$$÷2 \left(\begin{array}{c} \mathbf{10:6} \\ \mathbf{= 5:3} \end{array} \right) ÷2$$

A ratio of **5 : 3** means that for every five £1 coins there are three 2p coins.

The above ratio can also be written in the form **1 : n** by dividing both numbers in the ratio by 5…

$$÷5 \left(\begin{array}{c} \mathbf{5:3} \\ \mathbf{= 1:0.6} \end{array} \right) ÷5$$

It could also be written in the form n : 1 by dividing both numbers in the ratio by 3…

$$÷3 \left(\begin{array}{c} \mathbf{5:3} \\ \mathbf{= 1.6:1} \end{array} \right) ÷3$$

Examples

1. A bag of carrots weighs 300g and a bag of potatoes 1.5kg. Calculate the ratio of weight of carrots to weight of potatoes.

   Both quantities must be in the same units.
   1.5kg = 1.5 × 1000g **= 1500g**

   Ratio of weight of carrots to weight of potatoes is…

   $$÷300 \left(\begin{array}{c} \mathbf{300g : 1500g} \\ \mathbf{= 1 : 5} \end{array} \right) ÷300$$

2. On a map, a distance of 6km is shown as 3cm. Write the map distance to the real distance as a ratio in its simplest form.

   The ratio is 3cm : 6km
   = 3cm : 6 × 1000m × 100cm
   = 3 : 600 000
   = 1 : 200 000

   > Make the units the same for both parts of the ratio, then simplify by cancelling the units and any common factors

Ratios and Fractions

A ratio can be written as a fraction and vice versa.

Examples

1. If $\frac{2}{5}$ of a class are boys what is the ratio of boys to girls? Give your answer in the form 1 : n.

   The ratio of boys to girls is therefore…

   $$×5 \left(\begin{array}{c} \frac{2}{5} : \frac{3}{5} \\ \mathbf{= 2 : 3} \end{array} \right) ×5$$

   Written in the form **1 : n** it is…

   $$÷2 \left(\begin{array}{c} \mathbf{2 : 3} \\ \mathbf{= 1 : 1.5} \end{array} \right) ÷2$$

   In other words for any one boy in the class there are one and a half girls.

2. A drink is made by mixing cordial and water in the ratio 1 : 4. What fraction of the drink is cordial?

   1 part out of 5 (1 + 4) parts is cordial.
   The fraction of the drink that is cordial is $\frac{1}{5}$.

3. An archaeological dig unearths a ruined building with two outbuildings. Their lengths are in the ratio 1 : 1.6 : 2.2. What fraction of the whole is the middle section?

   Total parts = 4.8
   $\frac{1.6}{4.8} = \frac{16}{48} = \frac{4}{12} = \frac{1}{3}$

Calculations with Ratios

Dividing a Quantity in a Given Ratio

Examples

1 £60 is to be divided between Jon and Pat in the ratio 2 : 3. How much money does each one receive?

We need to divide £60 in the ratio 2 : 3.

The digits in the ratio represent parts. Jon gets 2 parts and Pat gets 3 parts. The total number of parts is 2 + 3 = 5 parts, which is equal to £60. Therefore…

$$\div 5 \left(\begin{array}{c} \textbf{5 parts = £60} \\ \textbf{1 part = £12} \end{array} \right) \div 5$$

Since we now know the 'value' of 1 part we can work out how much money Jon and Pat get.

Jon gets 2 parts = 2 × 12 = **£24**
Pat gets 3 parts = 3 × 12 = **£36**

> Check: £24 + £36 = £60

2 Three brothers aged 6, 9 and 15 decide to share a tin of toffees in the ratio of their ages. If the tin contains 240 toffees how many toffees does each brother get?

We need to divide 240 toffees in the ratio 6 : 9 : 15

> Whenever possible cancel down your ratio to make things simpler

$$\div 3 \left(\begin{array}{c} \textbf{6 : 9 : 15} \\ \textbf{= 2 : 3 : 5} \end{array} \right) \div 3$$

Total number of parts
= 2 + 3 + 5 = 10 parts

Therefore…

$$\div 10 \left(\begin{array}{c} \textbf{10 parts = 240 toffees} \\ \textbf{1 part = 24 toffees} \end{array} \right) \div 10$$

Brother aged 6 gets 2 × 24 = 48 toffees
Brother aged 9 gets 3 × 24 = 72 toffees
Brother aged 15 gets 5 × 24 = 120 toffees

> Check: 48 + 72 + 120 = 240 toffees

Increasing and Decreasing a Quantity in Direct Proportion

Examples

A recipe to make 10 flapjacks requires, among other ingredients, 180g of butter. How much butter does a cook need to use if they want to make…
a) 6 flapjacks?
b) 25 flapjacks?

This is an example of a quantity (e.g. butter) that increases or decreases in direct proportion to the amount of baking needed. The more baking needed the greater the amount of butter needed and vice versa.

The easiest way is to work out the amount of butter needed to make 1 flapjack.

$$\div 10 \left(\begin{array}{c} \textbf{10 flapjacks require 180g of butter} \\ \textbf{1 flapjack requires 18g of butter} \end{array} \right) \div 10$$

a) 6 flapjacks require
6 × 18g = **108g of butter**

b) 25 flapjacks require
25 × 18g = **450g of butter**

Changing with Inverse Proportion

Example

If 5 men can paint a factory in 12 days, how long would it take 4 men to paint the same factory?

The length of time required to paint the factory is inversely proportional to the number of men who paint it.
5 men take 12 days
∴ 1 man takes 60 days
∴ **4 men take 15 days**

Direct and Inverse Proportion

Direct Proportion

Two quantities are in **direct proportion** if, for example, when we double (or treble) one quantity the other quantity also doubles (or trebles).

Let us take two quantities, y and x, that are directly proportional. We can say that…

> y **is directly proportional to** x or $y \propto x$,

which means that…

> $y = kx$ where k is a constant, (i.e. a number that doesn't change).

Whenever you answer questions involving two quantities that are in direct proportion, the first thing to do is find the value of k to give you the formula for the relationship between the two quantities.

Example

The distance, d, travelled by a cyclist is directly proportional to t, the time of travel. If the cyclist travels 40 metres in 5 seconds, how far will the same cyclist travel in 12 seconds?

We know that $d \propto t$ or $d = kt$. The first thing we do is find the value for k.

Since $d = \textbf{40m}$ when $t = \textbf{5s}$ this gives us…

$40 = k \times 5$

$\therefore k = \dfrac{40}{5} = 8$

Our relationship now becomes…

$d = kt = 8 \times t$

$\quad = 8t$

We can now work out the value of d when $t = 12s$

$d = 8t$

$\quad = 8 \times 12$

$\quad = \textbf{96m}$

Inverse Proportion

Two quantities are in **inverse proportion** if, for example, when we double (or treble) one of the quantities the other quantity halves (or is divided by 3).

Let us take two quantities, y and x, that are inversely proportional. We can say that…

> y **is inversely proportional to** x or $y \propto \dfrac{1}{x}$,

which means that…

> $y = \dfrac{k}{x}$ where k is a constant

Whenever you answer questions involving two quantities that are inversely proportional, the first thing to do is find the value of k to give the formula for the relationship between the two quantities.

Example

A magnet is at a distance, $x$cm, from a metal object. The force, F Newtons, exerted by the magnet on the metal object is inversely proportional to the square of x.

a) When $x = 10$ and $F = 2$ find an equation expressing F in terms of x

b) find F when $x = 20$

c) find x when $F = 8$

a) $F \propto \dfrac{1}{x^2}$ so $F = \dfrac{k}{x^2}$

When $x = 10$, $F = 2$

$2 = \dfrac{k}{10^2}$

$k = 10^2 \times 2$ which gives $k = 200$

$F = \dfrac{\textbf{200}}{\textbf{x}^2}$

b) $F = \dfrac{200}{20^2} = \textbf{0.5}$

c) $8 = \dfrac{200}{x^2}$

$x^2 = \dfrac{200}{8} = 25$

$x = \textbf{5}$

Upper and Lower Bounds

What are Upper and Lower Bounds?

Sometimes measurements are given to a certain degree of accuracy. When this happens the actual measurement (or quantity) lies within a range that has its limits a certain value below (the **lower bound**) to a certain value above (the **upper bound**) the given measurement.

Accuracy of Given Measurement	Limits of Range Measurement Lies Between
Nearest 1000	500 below to 500 above the given measurement
Nearest 100	50 below to 50 above the given measurement
Nearest 10	5 below to 5 above the given measurement
Nearest 1	0.5 below to 0.5 above the given measurement
Nearest 0.1	0.05 below to 0.05 above the given measurement

Upper and Lower Bounds for the Four Rules of Number

If **A = 50** to the nearest **10** ($45 \leqslant A < 55$) and **B = 30** to the nearest **10** ($25 \leqslant B < 35$) then you get the following:

> The actual value cannot be equal to the upper bound because if it was, when rounded to the nearest 10, A = 60 and B = 40.

	Upper Bound	Lower Bound
A + B	55 + 35 = 90	45 + 25 = 70
A − B	55 − 25 = 30	45 − 35 = 10
A × B	55 × 35 = 1925	45 × 25 = 1125
$\dfrac{A}{B}$	55 ÷ 25 = 2.2	$\dfrac{45}{35}$ = 1.29 (2 d.p.)

Examples

1 A sprinter runs 200m in a time of 20.2 seconds, which is measured to the nearest 0.1 of a second. What are the upper and lower bounds of the time taken?

A measurement to the nearest 0.1s means that the actual measurement lies somewhere in a range 0.05s above or below the time of 20.2s. In other words there is a possible error of ± 0.05s on the recorded time.

Lower bound = 20.2s − 0.05s = 20.15s
Upper bound = 20.2s + 0.05s = 20.25s

This can be written: $\mathbf{20.15s \leqslant t < 20.25s}$
where **t = time taken**

> The actual value cannot be equal to the upper bound because if it was, the time to the nearest 0.1s would be 20.3s.

2 The rectangle below has dimensions 3cm by 2cm (each length is correct to the nearest centimetre). What is the smallest and largest area possible for the rectangle?

Area = 3cm × 2cm
= 6cm²

> The measurement of the base, **b**, can be anywhere in the range **2.5cm $\leqslant h <$ 3.5cm**

> The measurement of the height, **h**, can be anywhere in the range **1.5cm $\leqslant h <$ 2.5cm**

Smallest Area
A = 2.5cm × 1.5cm
= 3.75cm²

Largest Area
A = 3.5cm × 2.5cm
= 8.75cm²

Smallest Area = 3.75cm²
Largest Area = 8.75cm²

This can be written: $\mathbf{3.75cm^2 \leqslant A < 8.75cm^2}$
where **A = area of rectangle.**

Estimating and Checking

Estimating Answers

Answers to many calculations can be estimated by rounding off numbers within the calculations to 1 significant figure.

Examples

Estimate the answers to the following calculations:

1   71 + 18 − 26

$\approx$ 70 + 20 − 30

$\approx$ **60**

(Actual answer is 63)

2 $\dfrac{3.6 \times 10.4}{7.7 - 3.1}$

$\approx \dfrac{4 \times 10}{8 - 3}$

$\approx \dfrac{40}{5}$

$\approx$ **8**

(Actual answer is 8.14 (2 d.p.))

3 $\dfrac{413 \times 4.87}{0.189}$

$\approx \dfrac{400 \times 5}{0.2}$

$\approx \dfrac{2000}{0.2}$

$\approx$ **10 000**

(Actual answer is 10 600 (3 s.f.))

4 $\dfrac{57341}{0.00216}$

$= \dfrac{5.7341 \times 10^4}{2.16 \times 10^{-3}}$

> See page 13 for Standard Form

$\approx \dfrac{6 \times 10^4}{2 \times 10^{-3}}$

$\approx$ **3 × 10⁷**

(Actual answer is 2.65×10^7)

Checking your Answers for Accuracy

Answers to calculations can be checked for accuracy by starting with your answer and working backwards, reversing the operations.

Examples

1   8 × 7 = 56 $\longrightarrow$ $\dfrac{56}{8} = 7$ ✓ or $\dfrac{56}{7} = 8$ ✓

2   The table below shows the amount of money collected by a small local charity from October to December, using collecting tins at three different locations. Check it for accuracy.

Month	Location 1 (£)	Location 2 (£)	Location 3 (£)	Total (£)
Oct	28.08	16.73	18.23	63.04
Nov	32.96	21.01	18.16	72.13
Dec	26.12	19.57	16.03	61.72
Total	87.16	57.31	52.42	**196.89**

For this example, there are several ways of checking it for accuracy. You could check the totals for each month (rows) or the totals for each location (columns). Finally, check the overall total.

- 63.04 + 72.13 + 61.72 = **£196.89**
  196.89 − 61.72 − 72.13 = **£63.04** ✓

- 87.16 + 57.31 + 52.42 = **£196.89**
  196.89 − 52.42 − 57.31 = **£87.16** ✓

Expressions, Identities and Equations xy

Algebra is a branch of mathematics where letters and other symbols are used to represent numbers and quantities in expressions, equations, identities and formulae. Algebra follows the same rules as arithmetic.

Algebraic Expressions

An algebraic expression is a collection of connected letters, numbers and operations. Here are some simple expressions and their meanings.

Algebraic Expression	What it Means
$2a$	$a + a$ or $2 \times a$
ab	$a \times b$ (or $b \times a$)
$\frac{a}{b}$	$a \div b$
$3a - b$	$(3 \times a) - b$
c^2	$c \times c$
$4mn$	$4 \times m \times n$
x^2	$x \times x$
a^3	$a \times a \times a$
$4x^2y$	$4 \times x \times x \times y$
$(4a)^2$	$4a \times 4a$

A* Tip

You need to be confident at re-arranging formulae when working with more complex algebraic equations.

Collecting Like Terms

Many expressions can be simplified by collecting together like terms, e.g. all the x's or all the x^2's.

Examples

1. $a + 2a = \mathbf{3a}$

2. $5x - 8x + 7x = \mathbf{4x}$

> When your expression contains 'different' terms, rearrange and collect together all like terms before you simplify.

3. $\quad 6b + 3c - 4b$
   $= \underbrace{6b - 4b}_{\text{Like terms}} + 3c$
   $= \mathbf{2b + 3c}$

4. $\quad 4x + 7y - x - 3y$
   $= \underbrace{4x - x}_{\text{Like terms}} + \underbrace{7y - 3y}_{\text{Like terms}}$
   $= \mathbf{3x + 4y}$

5. $\quad 8x^2 - 4x + 3 - 3x^2 + 7x - 8$
   $= \underbrace{8x^2 - 3x^2}_{\text{Like terms}} \underbrace{- 4x + 7x}_{\text{Like terms}} \underbrace{+ 3 - 8}_{\text{Like terms}}$
   $= \mathbf{5x^2 + 3x - 5}$

6. $\quad 5pq - 7rs + 8qp + 2sr$
   $= \underbrace{5pq + 8qp}_{\substack{\text{Like terms} \\ \text{since '}pq\text{'} \\ \text{is the same} \\ \text{as '}qp\text{'}}} \underbrace{- 7rs + 2sr}_{\substack{\text{Like terms} \\ \text{since '}rs\text{' is} \\ \text{the same} \\ \text{as '}sr\text{'}}}$
   $= \mathbf{13pq - 5rs}$

Identities and Equations

The statement $\mathbf{4(x + 2) = 4x + 8}$ is an **identity**, which means that $4(x + 2)$ has the same value as $4x + 8$ whatever value of x is used.

Identities are very important because they allow us to replace an algebraic expression with an equivalent one that may be easier to work with.

The statement $\mathbf{3x + 4 = 19}$ is not true for all values of x. It is an example of an equation. The equation may be solved to give $x = 5$. Some equations have more than one solution.

Substitution

What is Substitution?

Substitution involves replacing the letters in a formula or expression with numbers and working out its value. This may involve working with positive or negative numbers, including fractions and decimals.

Examples

If $a = 3$, $b = 8$, $c = 20$ and $d = -4$, calculate the value of the following:

1 $2(a + b) - c$ | Substitute in your numbers

$= 2(3 + 8) - 20$ | Work out the bracket first

$= 2 \times 11 - 20$ | Then the multiplication

$= 22 - 20$ | Then the subtraction

$= 2$

2 $3d^2 + c$ | Substitute in your numbers

$= 3 \times (-4)^2 + 20$ | Work out the square first

$= 3 \times 16 + 20$ | Then the multiplication

$= 48 + 20$ | Then the addition

$= 68$

3 $\dfrac{c(d + 1)}{5}$ | Substitute in your numbers

$= \dfrac{20(-4 + 1)}{5}$ | Work out the bracket first

$= \dfrac{20 \times -3}{5}$ | Then the multiplication

$= \dfrac{-60}{5}$ | Then the division

$= -12$

4 $\dfrac{1}{2}d^3$ | Substitute in your numbers

$= \dfrac{1}{2} \times (-4)^3$ | Work out the cube first

$= \dfrac{1}{2} \times -64$ | Then the multiplication

$= -32$

Formulae

Some formulae are provided for you on a formulae sheet in the examination (see page 110). You may need to solve a problem by selecting the appropriate formula to use and substituting the given information.

Example

The diagram shows the positions of two coastguard stations, C1 and C2, from which a distress flare, F, is seen.

Calculate the distance of the distress flare from C1. Give your answer to 3 s.f.

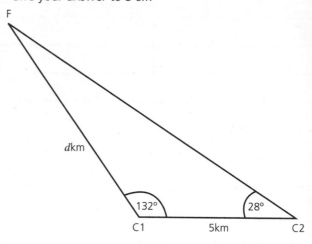

The appropriate formula to use in this case is the **sine rule** (see p.64).

Adapting the sine rule for this triangle gives

$$\frac{d}{\sin 28°} = \frac{5}{\sin F}$$

We need to find the size of angle F.

$$F = 180° - (132° + 28°) = 20°$$

$$\frac{d}{\sin 28°} = \frac{5}{\sin 20°}$$

$$d = \frac{5 \times \sin 28°}{\sin 20°} = 6.863\ldots$$

The distance of the distress flare from C1 is 6.86km

Brackets and Factorisation

xy

Multiplying Out Brackets

When we multiply out a bracket, everything which is inside the bracket must be multiplied by whatever is immediately outside the bracket.

Examples

1 $4(x + 3)$

$= 4 \times x + 4 \times 3$

$= \mathbf{4x + 12}$

2 $3x(4x^2 - 5)$

$= 3x \times 4x^2 + 3x \times \text{-}5$

$= \mathbf{12x^3 - 15x}$

> If your expression includes two brackets, it may result in like terms, which you need to collect together and simplify.

3 $2(4x + 3) + 5(x - 2)$

$= 2 \times 4x + 2 \times 3 + 5 \times x + 5 \times \text{-}2$

$= 8x + 6 + 5x - 10$

$= 8x + 5x + 6 - 10$

     Like terms   Like terms

$= \mathbf{13x - 4}$

4 $x(5 - x) + 4x(2x^2 + 3x)$

$= x \times 5 + x \times \text{-}x + 4x \times 2x^2 + 4x \times 3x$

$= 5x - x^2 + 8x^3 + 12x^2$

$= 8x^3 - x^2 + 12x^2 + 5x$

         Like terms

$= \mathbf{8x^3 + 11x^2 + 5x}$

> When you multiply out two brackets, make sure that each term in the second bracket is multiplied by each term in the first bracket.

5 $(x + 2)(x + 3)$

$= x(x + 3) + 2(x + 3)$

$= x \times x + x \times 3 + 2 \times x + 2 \times 3$

$= x^2 + 3x + 2x + 6$

         Like terms

$= \mathbf{x^2 + 5x + 6}$

6 $(3x - 2)^2$

$= (3x - 2)(3x - 2)$

$= 3x(3x - 2) - 2(3x - 2)$

$= 3x \times 3x + 3x \times \text{-}2 - 2 \times 3x - 2 \times \text{-}2$

$= 9x^2 - 6x - 6x + 4$

         Like terms

$= \mathbf{9x^2 - 12x + 4}$

Factorisation

Factorisation is the reverse process to multiplying out brackets. An expression is rewritten with a bracket by taking out highest common factors.

Examples

1 $4x + 6 = \mathbf{2(2x + 3)}$

> 2 is the highest common factor of both 4 and 6

2 $6x^2 + 8x = \mathbf{2x(3x + 4)}$

> $2x$ is the highest common factor of both $6x^2$ and $8x$

3 $9x^3y^2 - 6xy^3 = \mathbf{3xy^2(3x^2 - 2y)}$

> $3xy^2$ is the highest common factor of both $9x^3y^2$ and $6xy^3$

4 $x(2y + 3) + z(2y + 3) = \mathbf{(2y + 3)(x + z)}$

> $(2y + 3)$ is a common factor of $x(2y + 3)$ and $z(2y + 3)$

To check each of the examples above, multiply out each bracket. You should end up with the original expression.

It is useful to recognise:

$(a + b)^2 = a^2 + 2ab + b^2$ and $(a + b)(a - b) = a^2 - b^2$

Examples

1 $x^2 + 6x + 9 = \mathbf{(x + 3)^2}$

2 $9x^2 - 4y^2 = \mathbf{(3x + 2y)(3x - 2y)}$

A* Tips

When multiplying brackets out, examiners award marks for four terms, so show these terms before you simplify (usually to 3, occasionally to 2 terms).

If asked to 'factorise fully', this is a hint that more than one step is required to factorise completely.

Linear Equations

Linear Equations with the Unknown on One Side of the Equation

The following equations are all examples of linear equations since the highest power they contain is x^1 (i.e. x):

$$4x = 12$$
$$x + 3 = 7$$
$$2(x + 5) = 14$$

Each of these linear equations can be solved to find the 'unknown' value of x by collecting all the x's on one side and all the numbers on the other side. The simplest linear equation would involve one operation to solve it. Most however require at least two operations.

Examples

1 $6x = 15$

$$\frac{\cancel{6}x}{\cancel{6}} = \frac{15}{6}$$

$$x = 2.5$$

> Divide both sides of the equation by **6** to leave just x on the left-hand side.

2 $3x - 5 = 19$

$$3x - \cancel{5} + \cancel{5} = 19 + 5$$

$$\frac{\cancel{3}x}{\cancel{3}} = \frac{24}{3}$$

$$x = 8$$

> Add **5** to both sides of the equation to remove the **-5** from the left-hand side.

> Divide both sides of the equation by **3** to leave just x on the left-hand side.

3 $18 = 4(x + 9)$

$$18 = 4x + 36$$

$$18 - 36 = 4x + \cancel{36} - \cancel{36}$$

$$\frac{-18}{4} = \frac{\cancel{4}x}{\cancel{4}}$$

$$-4.5 = x$$

or $x = -4.5$

> Multiply out the bracket on the right-hand side.

> Subtract **36** from both sides of the equation to remove the **+36** on the right-hand side.

> Divide both sides of the equation by **4** to leave just x on the right-hand side.

4

$$\frac{4x + 3}{3} + \frac{5x - 3}{4} = 8$$

$$^4\cancel{12} \times \frac{(4x + 3)}{\cancel{3}} + {}^3\cancel{12} \times \frac{(5x - 3)}{\cancel{4}} = 12 \times 8$$

$$16x + 12 + 15x - 9 = 96$$

$$31x + 3 = 96$$

$$31x + \cancel{3} - \cancel{3} = 96 - 3$$

$$\frac{\cancel{31}x}{\cancel{31}} = \frac{93}{31}$$

$$x = 3$$

> Multiply all terms on both sides by **12**, which is the lowest common multiple of **3** and **4**, to remove the fractional values.

> Collect like terms on the left-hand side of the equation.

> Subtract **3** from both sides of the equation to remove the **+3** on the left-hand side.

> Divide both sides of the equation by **31** to leave just x on the left-hand side.

Linear Equations

xy

Linear Equations with the Unknown on Both Sides of the Equation

The following examples have the 'unknown', e.g. x, appearing on both sides of the equation. Once again they are solved by collecting all the x's on one side and all the numbers on the other side.

It does not really matter on which side of the equals sign you collect all the x's, it is your choice. In the examples below, they are collected on the side that has the most positive x's to start with. This ensures that you end up with a value for x rather than $-x$.

Examples

1

$$8x - 7 = 5x + 26$$

Subtract **5x** from both sides of the equation to leave all the x's on the left-hand side.

$$8x - 5x - 7 = 5x - 5x + 26$$

Add **7** to both sides of the equation to remove the **-7** on the left-hand side.

$$3x - 7 + 7 = 26 + 7$$

Divide both sides of the equation by **3** to leave just x on the left-hand side.

$$\frac{3x}{3} = \frac{33}{3}$$

$$x = 11$$

2

$$4(3x - 2) = 15x + 22$$

Multiply out the bracket on the left-hand side.

$$12x - 8 = 15x + 22$$

Subtract **12x** from both sides of the equation to leave all the x's on the right-hand side.

$$12x - 12x - 8 = 15x - 12x + 22$$

Subtract **22** from both sides of the equation to remove the **22** on the right-hand side.

$$-8 - 22 = 3x + 22 - 22$$

Divide both sides of the equation by **3** to leave just x on the right-hand side.

$$\frac{-30}{3} = \frac{3x}{3}$$

$$-10 = x$$

$$\text{or } x = \textbf{-10}$$

3

$$\frac{19 + x}{2} = 2 - x$$

Multiply all terms on both sides by **2** to remove the fractional value.

$$2 \times \frac{19 + x}{2} = 2 \times (2 - x)$$

Add **2x** to both sides of the equation to remove the **-2x** on the right-hand side.

$$19 + x = 4 - 2x$$

$$19 + x + 2x = 4 - 2x + 2x$$

Subtract **19** from both sides of the equation to remove the **19** on the left-hand side.

$$19 - 19 + 3x = 4 - 19$$

Divide both sides of the equation by **3** to leave just x on the right-hand side.

$$\frac{3x}{3} = \frac{-15}{3}$$

$$x = \textbf{-5}$$

Problem Solving Using Linear Equations

Problem solving using linear equations involves being given information, forming a linear equation from the information given and then solving the equation.

Example

The four angles of a quadrilateral are: a, $a + 20°$, $a + 40°$ and $a + 60°$. Calculate the size of each angle.

We know that the angles of a quadrilateral add up to **360°**. Therefore…

$$a + (a + 20) + (a + 40) + (a + 60) = 360$$

$$4a + 120 = 360°$$

$$4a = 240°$$ ← Subtract 120 from both sides

$$a = 60°$$ ← Divide both sides by 4

$a = \textbf{60°}$, $a + 20° = \textbf{80°}$, $a + 40° = \textbf{100°}$, $a + 60° = \textbf{120°}$

Formulae

Changing the Subject of a Formula

Formulae show the relationship between two or more changeable quantities (variables). They can be written in words, but most often symbols are used instead.

For example, the area of a circle is given by the formula: $A = \pi r^2$, which describes the relationship between the area of a circle A and its radius r.

Formulae can be rearranged to make a different letter the 'subject', e.g. $a = b + c$ has a as the subject since it is on one side by itself. If we wanted to make b or c the subject then we would need to rearrange the formula by moving terms from one side of the equals sign to the other.

Examples

1 Make b the subject of the following formula.

$$a = b + c$$
$$a - c = b + \cancel{c} - \cancel{c}$$
$$b = a - c$$

> Subtract c from both sides of the formula. This will remove the $+c$ on the right-hand side to leave b on its own.

> Rewrite the formula with b on the left-hand side.

2 Make x the subject of the following equation.

$$4(3x + 2y) = 5x + 2z$$
$$12x + 8y = 5x + 2z$$
$$12x - 5x + 8y = \cancel{5x} - \cancel{5x} + 2z$$
$$7x + \cancel{8y} - \cancel{8y} = 2z - 8y$$
$$\frac{\cancel{7}x}{\cancel{7}} = \frac{2z - 8y}{7}$$
$$x = \frac{2z - 8y}{7}$$

> Multiply out the bracket on the left-hand side.

> Subtract **5x** from both sides of the equation to remove the **5x** on the right-hand side.

> Subtract **8y** from both sides of the equation to remove the **+8y** on the left-hand side.

> Divide both sides of the equation by **7** to leave just x on the left-hand side.

3 Make r the subject of the following formula.

$$A = \pi r^2$$
$$\frac{A}{\pi} = \frac{\cancel{\pi} r^2}{\cancel{\pi}}$$
$$\sqrt{\frac{A}{\pi}} = \sqrt{r^2}$$
$$\sqrt{\frac{A}{\pi}} = r \text{ or } r = \sqrt{\frac{A}{\pi}}$$

> Divide both sides of the formula by π to remove the π on the right-hand side

> Take the square root of both sides of the formula to remove the 'square' and leave just r on the right-hand side.

> Rewrite the formula with r on the left-hand side.

4 Make x the subject of the following equation.

$$x + a = \frac{x + b}{c}$$
$$c(x + a) = x + b$$
$$cx + ca = x + b$$
$$cx - x = b - ca$$
$$x(c - 1) = b - ca$$
$$x = \frac{b - ca}{c - 1}$$

> Multiply all terms on both sides by c to remove the fractional value.

> Subtract ca and x from both sides of the equation so that x terms are on one side.

> Factorise and then rewrite the equation with x on the left-hand side.

Formulae

Using Formulae

Whenever you use a formula to work out an unknown quantity, all you are doing is substituting numbers for symbols.

Examples

1 The formula that converts a temperature reading from degrees Celsius (°C) into degrees Fahrenheit (°F) is:

$$F = \frac{9}{5}C + 32$$

What is the temperature in degrees Fahrenheit if the temperature in degrees Celsius is 25°C?

Our formula is: $F = \frac{9}{5}C + 32$

$F = \frac{9}{5} \times 25 + 32$ ← We now substitute into our formula a value for C, which is 25°C, to work out **F**

$F = 45 + 32$

$F = 77°F$

2 Calculate the height of a triangle of area 30cm² if the length of its base is 10cm.

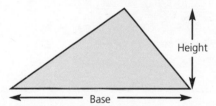

Height

Base

The area of a triangle is given by the formula:

$$A = \frac{b \times h}{2}$$

where **b** is the length of base and **h** is the height of the triangle.

Our formula is:

$A = \frac{b \times h}{2}$ — Since we want the subject of the formula to be **h**, we need to rearrange.

$A \times 2 = \frac{b \times h}{2} \times 2$ ← Multiply both sides by 2

$\frac{2A}{b} = \frac{b \times h}{b}$ ← Divide both sides by **b** to leave **h** on its own

$h = \frac{2A}{b}$

$h = \frac{2 \times 30}{10} = \frac{60}{10}$ — We can now substitute in values for **A** and **b** to find **h**

$h = 6cm$

Generating Formulae

Generating formulae means writing a formula using given information. You may then need to use the formula to work out an unknown quantity.

Example

Generate a formula for the sum of the interior angles of an irregular polygon.

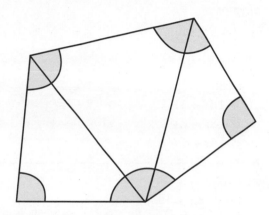

A pentagon (5 sides) can be divided into 3 triangles.

Sum of interior angles = 3 × 180°

$$= (5 - 2) \times 180°$$

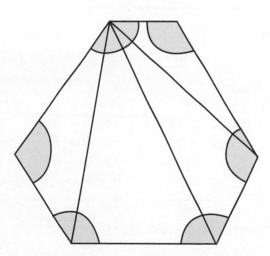

A hexagon (6 sides) can be divided into 4 triangles.

Sum of interior angles = 4 × 180°

$$= (6 - 2) \times 180°$$

In general: The sum of the interior angles of a polygon with n sides is $(n - 2) \times 180°$

Quadratic Expressions

What is a Quadratic Expression?

A quadratic expression is an expression in which the highest power of x is x^2, e.g. $x^2 + 6x + 5$, $x^2 - 9$ or $x^2 - 3x$. Quadratic expressions with terms that have no common factors give us two pairs of brackets when factorised, where each pair contains a letter (usually x) and a number.

For example, to factorise a quadratic expression such as $x^2 + 6x + 5$ the quickest approach is to...

① Write out two pairs of brackets and put an x in each one... $(x\ \ )(x\ \ )$

② Find two numbers that multiply to give the end number $+5$ $(+1 \times +5 = +5)$ and add up to give the middle number $+6$ $(+1 + +5 = +6)$

③ Insert your numbers – one in each bracket. Therefore, $x^2 + 6x + 5 = (x + 1)(x + 5)$

Examples

① $x^2 + 4x + 3$

$= (x + 1)(x + 3)$ ←

Write out your two pairs of brackets and put an x in each one

We now need two numbers that multiply to give $+3$ and also add up to $+4$

Check:
$(x + 1)(x + 3)$
$= x^2 + 3x + x + 3$
$= x^2 + 4x + 3$ ✓

$+1 \times +3 = +3$ ✓ and $+1 + +3 = +4$ ✓ (these are our two numbers)
$-1 \times -3 = +3$ ✓ and $-1 + -3 = -4$ ✗

② $x^2 - 8x + 7$

$= (x - 1)(x - 7)$ ←

Write out your two pairs of brackets and put an x in each one

We now need two numbers that multiply to give $+7$ and also add up to -8

Check:
$(x - 1)(x - 7)$
$= x^2 - 7x - 1x + 7$
$= x^2 - 8x + 7$ ✓

$+1 \times +7 = +7$ ✓ and $+1 + +7 = +8$ ✗
$-1 \times -7 = +7$ ✓ and $-1 + -7 = -8$ ✓ (these are our two numbers)

③ $x^2 + 5x - 6$

$= (x - 1)(x + 6)$ ←

Write out your two pairs of brackets and put an x in each one

We now need two numbers that multiply to give -6 and also add up to $+5$

Check:
$(x - 1)(x + 6)$
$= x^2 + 6x - x - 6$
$= x^2 + 5x - 6$ ✓

$+1 \times -6 = -6$ ✓ and $+1 + -6 = -5$ ✗
$-1 \times +6 = -6$ ✓ and $-1 + +6 = +5$ ✓ (these are our two numbers)
$+2 \times -3 = -6$ ✓ and $+2 + -3 = -1$ ✗
$-2 \times +3 = -6$ ✓ and $-2 + +3 = +1$ ✗

Difference of Two Squares

There are some quadratic expressions that don't have any x's in the middle and end in – **'a number'^{2}**. These expressions can also be factorised. Expressions such as $x^2 - 1^2$, $x^2 - 2^2$, $x^2 - 3^2$, $x^2 - 4^2$ and so on, are known as the 'difference of two squares'.

Again, you should check your answers by multiplying out the brackets. If you do so you should end up with the original expression.

Examples

① $x^2 - 1 = x^2 - 1^2 = (x + 1)(x - 1)$

② $x^2 - 4 = x^2 - 2^2 = (x + 2)(x - 2)$

③ $x^2 - 9 = x^2 - 3^2 = (x + 3)(x - 3)$

④ $x^2 - 16 = x^2 - 4^2 = (x + 4)(x - 4)$

Quadratic Equations

xy

Solving Quadratic Equations by Factorisation

The following equations are all examples of quadratic equations (i.e. their highest power is x^2):

$x^2 + 4x + 3 = 0$

$x^2 - 16 = 0$

$2x^2 + 5x - 3 = 0$

To solve a quadratic equation by factorisation:

(1) Factorise the quadratic expression within the equation to form two pairs of brackets (see pages 32).

(2) Treat each pair of brackets as a separate linear equation equal to 0 (zero).

Examples

1 Factorise

$x^2 - 6x + 5 = 0$

To factorise the quadratic expression within the equation, we need two numbers that multiply to give **+5** and also add up to **-6**.

$+1 \times +5 = +5$ ✓ and $+1 + +5 = +6$ ✗

$-1 \times -5 = +5$ ✓ and $-1 + -5 = -6$ ✓ (these are our two numbers)

Our factorised quadratic equation now looks like...

$(x - 1)(x - 5) = 0$

• We now have two brackets which when multiplied together are equal to 0 (zero).
• This is only possible if one or both of the two brackets is also equal to 0 (zero).
• We now treat each bracket as a separate linear equation equal to 0 (zero).

And so...

$(x - 1) = 0$

$x - \cancel{1} + \cancel{1} = 0 + 1$

$x = 1$ ... is one solution

Check: $x = 1$

$x^2 - 6x + 5 = 0$

$1^2 - 6 \times 1 + 5 = 0$

$1 - 6 + 5 = 0$ ✓

or

$(x - 5) = 0$

$x - \cancel{5} + \cancel{5} = 0 + 5$

$x = 5$ ... is the other

Check: $x = 5$

$x^2 - 6x + 5 = 0$

$5^2 - 6 \times 5 + 5 = 0$

$25 - 30 + 5 = 0$ ✓

2 Factorise

$3x^2 + 13x + 4 = 0$

Find two numbers that multiply to give (3 x 4). i.e. 12, and add up to 13. In this case the numbers are 1 and 12.

Split the '13x' term, $3x^2 + x + 12x + 4$

Factorise in pairs, $x(3x + 1) + 4(3x + 1)$

$(3x + 1)$ is common, $(3x + 1)(x + 4)$

Our factorised quadratic equation now looks like...

$(3x + 1)(x + 4) = 0$

And so...

$(3x + 1) = 0$

$3x + \cancel{1} - \cancel{1} = 0 - 1$

$3x = -1$

$x = \dfrac{-1}{3}$ ... is one solution

Check:

$x = \dfrac{-1}{3}$

$3x^2 + 13x + 4 = 0$

$3 \times (\tfrac{-1}{3})^2 + 13 \times (\tfrac{-1}{3}) + 4 = 0$

$0.3\dot{3} + (-4.\dot{3}) + 4 = 0$ ✓

or

$(x + 4) = 0$

$x + \cancel{4} - \cancel{4} = 0 - 4$

$x = -4$ ... is the other

Check:

$x = -4$

$3x^2 + 13x + 4 = 0$

$3 \times (-4)^2 + 13 \times (-4) + 4 = 0$

$48 + -52 + 4 = 0$ ✓

Quadratic Equations

Solving Quadratic Equations by Completing the Square

Solving quadratic equations by completing the square is another method that can be used to solve quadratic equations and is particularly useful when the solutions are not integers. Although you can use this method, you should always try and factorise the quadratic expression within the quadratic equation first (as on page 33) in order to solve the equation.

1. Rearrange your equation so all the terms involving x^2 and x are on one side and your number is on the other side.
2. Write the terms in the form... $(x + a \text{ 'number'})^2$. Your 'number' should have a value **half** that of the number before the term involving x.
3. Now expand the square bracket to get the original terms involving x^2 and x, **plus a new 'number'**. To balance the equation, add the new 'number' onto the other side too.
4. Take the square root of both sides of your equation to get two separate linear equations which you then solve.

Examples

1

$$x^2 - 6x + 5 = 0$$
$$x^2 - 6x = -5$$
$$(x - 3)^2 = -5 + 9$$
$$(x - 3)^2 = 4$$
$$\sqrt{(x - 3)^2} = \sqrt{4}$$
$$x - 3 = \pm 2$$

> Rearrange your equation.
>
> Complete the square and balance the equation by adding **+9** to the right-hand side.
> $[(x - 3)^2 = (x - 3)(x - 3) = x^2 - 6x + 9]$
>
> Take the square root of both sides.

> We now have two separate linear equations:
> $x - 3 = +2$ and $x - 3 = -2$

One solution...
$$x - 3 = +2$$
$$x = 5$$

Check:
$$x^2 - 6x + 5 = 0$$
$$5^2 - 6 \times 5 + 5 = 0$$
$$25 - 30 + 5 = 0 ✓$$

... or another solution
$$x - 3 = -2$$
$$x = 1$$

Check:
$$x^2 - 6x + 5 = 0$$
$$1^2 - 6 \times 1 + 5 = 0$$
$$1 - 6 + 5 = 0 ✓$$

2

$$x^2 - 4x - 6 = 0$$
$$x^2 - 4x = 6$$
$$(x - 2)^2 = 6 + 4$$
$$(x - 2)^2 = 10$$
$$\sqrt{(x - 2)^2} = \sqrt{10}$$
$$x - 2 = \pm 3.16$$

> Rearrange your equation.
>
> Complete the square and balance the equation by adding **+4** to the right-hand side.
> $[(x - 2)^2 = (x - 2)(x - 2) = x^2 - 4x + 4]$
>
> Take the square root of both sides.

> We now have two separate linear equations:
> $x - 2 = +3.16$ and $x - 2 = -3.16$

One solution...
$$x - 2 = +3.16$$
$$x = 5.16$$

Check:
$$x^2 - 4x - 6 = 0$$
$$(5.16)^2 - (4 \times 5.16) - 6 = 0$$
$$26.63 - 20.64 - 6 = 0 ✓$$

... or another solution
$$x - 2 = -3.16$$
$$x = -1.16$$

Check:
$$x^2 - 4x - 6 = 0$$
$$(-1.16)^2 - (4 \times -1.16) - 6 = 0$$
$$1.35 + 4.64 - 6 = 0 ✓$$

Quadratic Equations

xy

Solving Quadratic Equations by Using the Formula

This formula can be used to solve quadratic equations:

$$x = \frac{-b \pm \sqrt{b^2 - 4ac}}{2a}$$

This method is again useful when the solutions are not whole numbers. It can be used to solve equations in the form $ax^2 + bx + c = 0$

A* Tips

If when handling quadratics, you are asked to round off to decimal places, it is a clue that factorising will not work, and you should use the formula. Factorisation is worth less than using the formula, so check how many marks are being offered.

Examples

1 $x^2 - 6x + 5 = 0$

In this case, $a = 1$, $b = -6$ and $c = 5$. If we now substitute these values into the formula:

$$x = \frac{-b \pm \sqrt{b^2 - 4ac}}{2a}$$

$$x = \frac{-(-6) \pm \sqrt{(-6)^2 - (4 \times 1 \times 5)}}{2 \times 1}$$

$$x = \frac{6 \pm \sqrt{36 - 20}}{2}$$

$$x = \frac{6 \pm \sqrt{16}}{2}$$

$$x = \frac{6 \pm 4}{2}$$

> We now have two separate linear equations.

And so...

$$x = \frac{6 + 4}{2}$$

$$x = \frac{10}{2}$$

$$x = 5$$

or...

$$x = \frac{6 - 4}{2}$$

$$x = \frac{2}{2}$$

$$x = 1$$

Check:
$x^2 - 6x + 5 = 0$
$(5)^2 - (6 \times 5) + 5 = 0$
$25 - 30 + 5 = 0$ ✓

Check:
$x^2 - 6x + 5 = 0$
$(1)^2 - (6 \times 1) + 5 = 0$
$1 - 6 + 5 = 0$ ✓

2 $5x^2 + 2x - 4 = 0$

Therefore, $a = 5$, $b = 2$ and $c = -4$. If we now substitute these values into the formula:

$$x = \frac{-b \pm \sqrt{b^2 - 4ac}}{2a}$$

$$x = \frac{-2 \pm \sqrt{(2)^2 - (4 \times 5 \times -4)}}{2 \times 5}$$

$$x = \frac{-2 \pm \sqrt{4 + 80}}{10}$$

$$x = \frac{-2 \pm \sqrt{84}}{10}$$

$$x = \frac{-2 \pm 9.165}{10}$$

> We now have two separate linear equations.

And so...

$$x = \frac{-2 + 9.165}{10}$$

$$x = \frac{7.165}{10}$$

$$x = 0.72 \text{ (to 2 d.p.)}$$

or...

$$x = \frac{-2 - 9.165}{10}$$

$$x = \frac{-11.165}{10}$$

$$x = -1.12 \text{ (to 2 d.p.)}$$

(allowing for rounding errors)

Check:
$5x^2 + 2x - 4 = 0$
$5(0.72)^2 + (2 \times 0.72) - 4 = 0$
$2.59 + 1.44 - 4 = 0$ ✓

Check:
$5x^2 + 2x - 4 = 0$
$5(-1.12)^2 + (2 \times -1.12) - 4 = 0$
$6.27 - 2.24 - 4 = 0$ ✓

Trial and Improvement

Solving Equations by Trial and Improvement

Solving equations by trial and improvement can be used to find a solution to any equation. As the name suggests we trial a possible solution by substituting its value into the equation.

The process is then repeated using a different possible solution and so on. The idea is that each subsequent trial is an improvement on the previous trial.

Examples

1 The equation $x^3 + x = 20$ has a solution somewhere between $x = 2$ and $x = 3$. By trial and improvement, calculate a solution to the equation to 2 decimal places.

Since we are told that there is a solution between $x = 2$ and $x = 3$ we will substitute their values into our equation to see what $x^3 + x$ gives us. Remember we want its value to be equal to **20**.

x	$x^3 + x$	Comment
2	$2^3 + 2$ $= 8 + 2$ $= 10$	Less than 20
3	$3^3 + 3$ $= 27 + 3$ $= 30$	More than 20
Try 2.5	$2.5^3 + 2.5$ $= 15.625 + 2.5$ $= 18.125$	Less than 20
Try 2.6	$2.6^3 + 2.6$ $= 17.576 + 2.6$ $= 20.176$	More than 20
Try 2.55	$2.55^3 + 2.55$ $= 16.581375 + 2.55$ $= 19.131375$	Less than 20
Try 2.58	$2.58^3 + 2.58$ $= 17.173512 + 2.58$ $= 19.753512$	Less than 20
Try 2.59	$2.59^3 + 2.59$ $= 17.373979 + 2.59$ $= 19.963979$	Just less than 20
Try 2.595	$2.595^3 + 2.595$ $= 17.474795 + 2.595$ $= 20.069795$	Just more than 20

So $x = 2.59$ (to 2 d.p.) since the last trial above, $x = 2.595$, is more than 20.

If the last trial had been less than 20 then $x = 2.60$ (to 2 d.p.) would be the solution. (It is important to try the middle value **2.595**).

2 The equation $x^2 - \dfrac{12}{x} = 10$ has a solution somewhere between $x = 3$ and $x = 4$. By trial and improvement, calculate a solution to the equation to 2 decimal places.

x	$x^2 - \dfrac{12}{x}$	Comment
3	$3^2 - \frac{12}{3}$ $= 9 - 4$ $= 5$	Less than 10
4	$4^2 - \frac{12}{4}$ $= 16 - 3$ $= 13$	More than 10
Try 3.5	$3.5^2 - \frac{12}{3.5}$ $= 12.25 - 3.4285714$ $= 8.821429$	Less than 10
Try 3.6	$3.6^2 - \frac{12}{3.6}$ $= 12.96 - 3.3333333$ $= 9.626667$	Less than 10
Try 3.7	$3.7^2 - \frac{12}{3.7}$ $= 13.69 - 3.2432432$ $= 10.446757$	More than 10
Try 3.65	$3.65^2 - \frac{12}{3.65}$ $= 13.3225 - 3.2876712$ $= 10.034829$	More than 10
Try 3.64	$3.64^2 - \frac{12}{3.64}$ $= 13.2496 - 3.2967033$ $= 9.952897$	Less than 10
Try 3.645	$3.645^2 - \frac{12}{3.645}$ $= 13.286025 - 3.2921811$ $= 9.993844$	Just less than 10

So $x = 3.65$ (to 2 d.p.) since the last trial above, $x = 3.645$, is less than 10.

If the last trial had been more than 10 then $x = 3.64$ (to 2 d.p.) would be the solution. (It is important to try the middle value **3.645**).

Sequences

Number Patterns and Sequences

A number pattern or sequence is a series of numbers that follow a rule. Each number in a sequence is called a **term**, where the first number in the sequence is called the **1st term** and so on.

Examples

1st term	2nd term	3rd term	4th term
2,	**6,**	**10,**	**14,...**

+4   +4   +4

The rule is that each term is **4 more** than the previous term. These terms have a common difference of +4

The next two terms

... 18,   22, ...

+4

20,	**17,**	**14,**	**11,...**

-3   -3   -3

The rule is that each term is **3 less** than the previous term. These terms have a common difference of -3

... 8,   5, ...

-3

1,	**3,**	**9,**	**27,...**

×3   ×3   ×3

The rule is that each term is **3 times** the previous term. These terms don't have a common difference between them

...81,   243,...

×3

A sequence can also be a series of diagrams.

+2   +2   +2

Each diagram (term) has **2 more** boxes in it than the previous diagram. These diagrams have a common difference of +2

+2

+1   +1   +1

Each diagram (term) has **1 more** match in it than the previous diagram. These diagrams have a common difference of +1

+1

Examples

1 Squared integers

1,	**4,**	**9,**	**16,...**
($1^2 = 1$)	($2^2 = 4$)	($3^2 = 9$)	($4^2 = 16$)

2 Triangular numbers

1,	**3,**	**6,**	**10,...**

+2   +3   +4

3 Powers of 2

1,	**2,**	**4,**	**8, ...**
($2^0 = 1$)	($2^1 = 2$)	($2^2 = 4$)	($2^3 = 8$)

4 Powers of 10

1,	**10,**	**100,**	**1000,...**
($10^0 = 1$)	($10^1 = 10$)	($10^2 = 100$)	($10^3 = 1000$)

Sequences

The nth Term of a Sequence

The nth term is a formula that enables us to generate any term within a particular sequence.

Example

Let our sequence of numbers have an **nth term = $2n + 2$** where **n** is the position of the term, i.e. the first term has **$n = 1$**, the second term has **$n = 2$** and so on. This formula now enables us to generate any term simply by substituting our value for n into the formula.

$$n\text{th term } = 2n + 2$$
$$\text{1st term } = 2 \times 1 + 2 = 4$$
$$\text{2nd term } = 2 \times 2 + 2 = 6$$
$$\text{3rd term } = 2 \times 3 + 2 = 8$$
$$\text{4th term } = 2 \times 4 + 2 = 10$$
$$\text{100th term } = 2 \times 100 + 2 = 202$$

So, our sequence of numbers would look like…
4, 6, 8, 10, …

Finding the nth term of an Arithmetic Sequence

A sequence where there is a common difference between the terms can be described by a linear algebraic expression. The general formula for the nth term of these sequences is as follows:

---

nth term = $an + b$

where **a** is the common difference between the terms and **b** is a constant.

The first thing you do is determine the value of **a**. To then find **b** substitute the value for the 1st term, **$n = 1$** and **a** into the formula.

Examples

1

5,   7,   9,   11,…

+2   +2   +2

These terms have a common difference of **+2** and so **$a = 2$**. If we take the 1st term then **$n = 1$** and it has a value of **5**. We then substitute these values into the formula…

$$n\text{th term } = an + b$$
$$5 = 2 \times 1 + b$$

$$b = 5 - 2$$
$$= 3$$

Therefore, **nth term = $2n + 3$**

To check:
2nd term = $2 \times 2 + 3 = 4 + 3 = 7$ ✓
3rd term = $2 \times 3 + 3 = 6 + 3 = 9$ ✓

2 20,   17,   14,   11,…

−3   −3   −3

These terms have a common difference of **−3** and so **$a = -3$**. If we take the 1st term then **$n = 1$** and it has a value of **20**. We then substitute these values into the formula…

$$n\text{th term } = an + b$$
$$20 = -3 \times 1 + b$$

$$b = 20 + 3$$
$$= 23$$

Therefore, **nth term = $-3n + 23$**

To check:
2nd term = $-3 \times 2 + 23 = -6 + 23 = 17$ ✓
3rd term = $-3 \times 3 + 23 = -9 + 23 = 14$ ✓

Straight Line Graphs

Graphs of Linear Functions

A linear function, e.g. **$y = x$, $y = 2x - 1$, $y = 0.5x + 1$,** (i.e. a function that may be written in the form $ax + b$, where a and b are constants) will always give you a straight line graph when drawn.

To draw the graph of a linear function you only need to plot a minimum of three points.

Examples

1 Draw the graph of **$y = 2x - 1$** for values of x between **-2** and **2** (this may be written **-2 $\leqslant$ x $\leqslant$ 2**).

Firstly, we need to pick at least 3 values of x, within the range, so that we can work out their y values. The two extreme values of x and one in the middle will do. Draw a table of results as follows:

Table of results for $y = 2x - 1$			
x	-2	0	2
$2x$	(2 × -2 =) -4	(2 × 0 =) 0	(2 × 2 =) 4
-1	-1	-1	-1
$y = 2x - 1$	(-4 – 1 =) **-5**	(0 – 1 =) **-1**	(4 – 1 =) **3**

We now have the coordinates of 3 points – (-2,-5), (0,-1) and (2,3) – and can plot our graph.

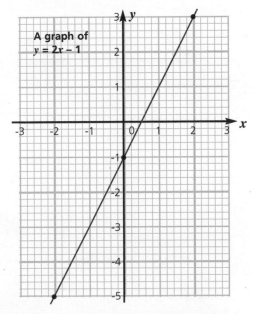

A graph of $y = 2x - 1$

Remember... Your straight line must pass through all 3 points! If it doesn't then one of your points is wrong. You can either check your table again or better still work out the coordinates of another point, e.g. when $x = -1$ or $x = 1$.

2 Draw the graph of **$2y + x = 4$** for values of x between **-2** and **2**.

The first thing we have to do is rearrange the function to make y the subject. When we have done that we can draw a table of results.

$$2y + x = 4$$
$$2y + \cancel{x} - \cancel{x} = -x + 4 \quad \longleftarrow \boxed{\text{Subtract } x \text{ from both sides}}$$
$$\frac{\cancel{2}y}{\cancel{2}} = \frac{-x}{2} + \frac{4}{2} \quad \longleftarrow \boxed{\text{Divide both sides by 2}}$$

To give us... **$y = -0.5x + 2$**

Table of results for $y = -0.5x + 2$			
x	-2	0	2
$-0.5x$	(-0.5 × -2 =) 1	(-0.5 × 0 =) 0	(-0.5 × 2 =) -1
+ 2	+2	+2	+2
$y = -0.5x + 2$	(1 + 2 =) **3**	(0 + 2 =) **2**	(-1 + 2 =) **1**

We now have the coordinates of 3 points – (-2,3), (0,2) and (2,1) – and can plot our graph.

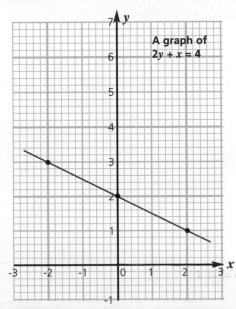

A graph of $2y + x = 4$

Gradients

$y = mx + c$

The general equation of any line **not** parallel to the y-axis may be written in the form $y = mx + c$ where...

- m is the value of the gradient. The gradient or slope of a line is a measure of the steepness of the line; the bigger the gradient the steeper the line. The gradient of a line can either be positive or negative, depending on which way the line slopes.

- c is the value of the intercept. The intercept of a line is simply the y value at the point where the line crosses the y-axis (i.e. when $x = 0$).

Each of the graphs below have the same intercept ($c = +1$) but different gradients. The gradient of the lines in graph ❶ and ❷ are both positive with graph ❷ having a steeper slope ($m = 3$ as compared to $m = 2$ for graph ❶). The line in graph ❸ has a negative gradient ($m = -2$) and so it slopes in the opposite direction to the other two graphs.

Remember, a positive (+) gradient goes **up** from left to right (as we read) whereas a negative (-) gradient goes **down** from left to right.

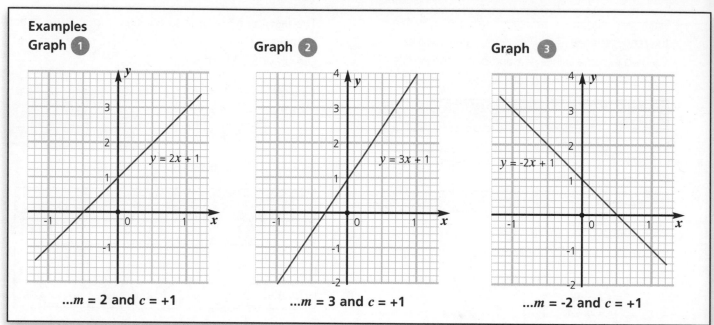

Examples

Graph ❶   **Graph** ❷   **Graph** ❸

...$m = 2$ and $c = +1$ ...$m = 3$ and $c = +1$ ...$m = -2$ and $c = +1$

Gradients of Parallel and Perpendicular Lines

Lines represented by equations that have the same gradient will be parallel even if each equation has a different intercept.

If two lines are perpendicular to each other, the product of their gradient = -1.

For example, lines represented by $y = 2x + 2$ and $y = 2x - 1$ are parallel as both have gradient **2**.

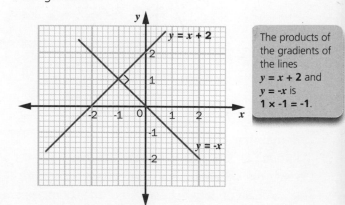

The products of the gradients of the lines $y = x + 2$ and $y = -x$ is $1 \times -1 = -1$.

Linear Inequalities

xy

Four Kinds of Inequality

1 > which means 'Greater than'

e.g. if $x > 4$ then x can have any value 'greater than' **4** but it can't have a value equal to **4**.

This inequality can be shown using a number line. An open O circle means that $x = 4$ is not included in the inequality.

2 ≥ which means 'Greater than or Equal to'

e.g. if $x \geq 4$ then x can have any value 'greater than' **4** and its value can also be 'equal to' **4**.

This inequality can be shown using a number line. A closed ● circle means that $x = 4$ is included in the inequality.

3 < which means 'Less than'

e.g. if $x < 1$ then x can have any value 'less than' **1** but it can't have a value equal to **1**.

This inequality can be shown using a number line. An open O circle means that $x = 1$ is not included in the inequality.

4 ≤ which means 'Less than or Equal to'

e.g. if $x \leq 1$ then x can have any value 'less than' **1** and its value can also be 'equal to' **1**.

This inequality can be shown using a number line. A closed ● circle means that $x = 1$ is included in the inequality.

Number lines can also be used to show a combination of inequalities.

Examples

1 $-2 \leq x < 5$

2 $1 < x \leq 4$

Solving Linear Inequalities

Solving linear inequalities is just like solving linear equations except we have an inequality sign instead of the equals sign.

Example

$$x + 2 < 8$$
$$x + \cancel{2} - \cancel{2} < 8 - 2$$
$$x < 6$$

However, if you multiply or divide an inequality by a negative number then you must always reverse the direction of the inequality sign.

Example

$$\frac{-x}{4} \leq 1.5$$
$$\frac{\cancel{-}x}{\cancel{4}} \times \cancel{-4} \geq 1.5 \times -4$$
$$x \geq -6$$

> Multiply both sides by -4… inequality sign reverses direction (i.e. ≤ becomes ≥)

If there is more than one inequality you should solve the two inequalities separately.

Example

$x + 1 < 2x < x + 2$

Solve the two inequalities separately:

$x + 1 < 2x$	$2x < x + 2$
$1 < x$	$x < 2$

∴ The solution is **$1 < x < 2$**

Linear Inequalities

Illustrating Linear Inequalities Graphically

Any linear inequality can be illustrated graphically. You have to do the following:

1 Treat the inequality as an equation with an equal (=) sign and draw its graph. Where a '>' or '<' inequality is used the line drawn is a dotted line; for a '≥' or '≤' inequality the line drawn is a solid line.

2 Label and shade in the region that satisfies the inequality or inequalities.

Example

Illustrate $x < 4$ graphically. Label and shade the region that satisfies the inequality.

- Firstly draw the graph of $x = 4$ (remember to draw a dotted line).
- To determine the region that satisfies the inequality, pick two points (we've labelled them A and B) one on each side of the line $x = 4$ (see graph).
- Label and shade the region that satisfies the inequality.

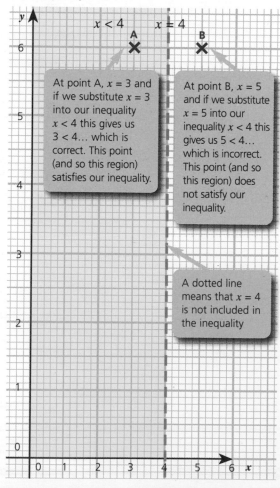

At point A, $x = 3$ and if we substitute $x = 3$ into our inequality $x < 4$ this gives us $3 < 4$... which is correct. This point (and so this region) satisfies our inequality.

At point B, $x = 5$ and if we substitute $x = 5$ into our inequality $x < 4$ this gives us $5 < 4$... which is incorrect. This point (and so this region) does not satisfy our inequality.

A dotted line means that $x = 4$ is not included in the inequality

Representing Linear Inequalities in Two Variables

Example

Illustrate $y \geq 1$, $y < 2x$ and $x + y \leq 6$ graphically. Label and shade the single region that is satisfied by all of these inequalities.

Draw the graph of…

… $y = 1$

… $y = 2x$. Make a simple table of results.

x	0	2	4
$y = 2x$	0	4	8

… $x + y = 6$. Rearrange to give y on its own and make a simple table of results.

x	0	3	6
$y = 6 - x$	6	3	0

Label and shade the region that satisfies all three inequalities.

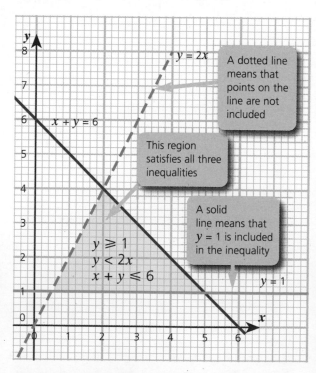

A dotted line means that points on the line are not included

This region satisfies all three inequalities

A solid line means that $y = 1$ is included in the inequality

$y \geq 1$
$y < 2x$
$x + y \leq 6$

N.B. You may be asked to shade the 'unwanted region', particularly when representing several inequalities on the same diagram. The region left unshaded in this case will be the region that satisfies all of the inequalities.

Simultaneous Equations

Solving Simultaneous Equations by Elimination

Simultaneous equations are when you work with two related equations (e.g. where x and y represent the same thing in both equations) at the same time. Individually the equations do not provide enough information for you to solve them (i.e. to find the values of x and y). However, when you work with both of them 'simultaneously' they provide enough combined information to solve them.

To solve simultaneous equations we need both equations to have the same coefficients (number in front of the unknown values, e.g. x and y).

- If these two numbers have the same sign (i.e. both positive or both negative) then we subtract one equation from the other.
- If these two numbers have different signs (i.e. one is positive and one is negative) then we add the two equations together.

Examples

1 Solve the two simultaneous equations:
$4x + 2y = 14$ and $x + 2y = 8$

Label the equations ① and ②

$$4x + 2y = 14 \quad ①$$
$$x + 2y = 8 \quad ②$$

Equations ① and ② both have the same number of y's with the same sign (+), so we subtract one equation from the other to remove the y's.

Subtract
①－②
$$4x + 2y = 14 \quad ①$$
$$\underline{- (x + 2y = 8) \quad ②}$$
$$3x \quad = 6$$

To give us: $x = \mathbf{2}$

To find the value of y, substitute $x = 2$ back into equation ① or ② (pick the easiest).
If we take equation ② ...

$$x + 2y = 8$$
$$2 + 2y = 8$$
$$2y = 8 - 2$$
$$2y = 6$$
$$y = \mathbf{3}$$

To check our solutions substitute $x = 2$ and $y = 3$ into equation ① since we used equation ② to find the value of y.

$4x + 2y = 14$
$4 \times 2 + 2 \times 3 = 14$
$8 + 6 = 14$ ✔

2 Solve the two simultaneous equations:
$2x + 3y = 5$ and $5x - 2y = -16$

Label the equations ① and ②

$$2x + 3y = 5 \quad ①$$
$$5x - 2y = -16 \quad ②$$

Multiply equation ① by 5 and multiply equation ② by 2. Equation ① now becomes equation ③ and equation ② has becomes equation ④.

$① \times 5 \longrightarrow 10x + 15y = 25 \quad ③$
$② \times 2 \longrightarrow 10x - 4y = -32 \quad ④$

Equations ③ and ④ now have the same number of x's, so we subtract one equation from the other to remove the x's

Subtract
③－④
$$10x + 15y = 25 \quad ③$$
$$\underline{- 10x - 4y = -32 \quad ④}$$
$$19y = 57$$

To give us: $y = \mathbf{3}$

To find the value of x, substitute $y = 3$ into equation ①,

$$2x + 3y = 5$$
$$2x + 3 \times 3 = 5$$
$$2x = 5 - 9$$
$$2x = -4$$
$$x = \mathbf{-2}$$

To check our solutions substitute $x = -2$ and $y = 3$ into equation ② since we used equation ① to find the value of x. If we take equation ② ...

$5x - 2y = -16$
$-10 - 6 = -16$ ✔

A* Tip

You should not assume that solutions to equations will be whole numbers, but if you do get strange answers it may be that you've gone wrong somewhere, so check your workings.

Simultaneous Equations

Solving Linear Simultaneous Equations Graphically

Simultaneous equations can also be solved graphically. Linear equations when plotted give us straight line graphs.

At the point of intersection the corresponding x and y values are the solutions of the simultaneous equations.

If the lines are parallel then there is no point of intersection and the equations cannot be solved simultaneously, e.g. $x + y = 6$ and $x + y = 4$.

Examples

1 Solve graphically the two simultaneous equations $x + y = 5$ and $2x + y = 7$ where the value of x lies in the range $1 \leqslant x \leqslant 5$

> For each equation we need 3 corresponding values of x and y which can then be plotted so that we can draw our graph. This may mean rearranging an equation to give us y on its own.

Our First Equation

$x + y = 5$
$\therefore y = 5 - x$

x	1	3	5
$y = 5 - x$	(5 − 1 =) **4**	(5 − 3 =) **2**	(5 − 5 =) **0**

Our Second Equation

$2x + y = 7$
$\therefore y = 7 - 2x$

x	1	3	5
$y = 7 - 2x$	(7 − 2×1 =) **5**	(7 − 2×3 =) **1**	(7 − 2×5 =) **-3**

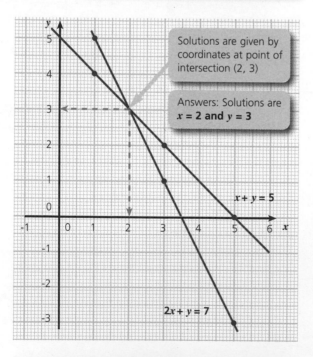

Solutions are given by coordinates at point of intersection (2, 3)

Answers: Solutions are $x = 2$ and $y = 3$

> To check our solutions substitute $x = 2$ and $y = 3$ into our two equations:
> $x + y = 5$: $2 + 3 = 5$ ✔
> $2x + y = 7$: $2 \times 2 + 3 = 7$: $4 + 3 = 7$ ✔

2 Solve graphically the two simultaneous equations $4x = y + 3$ and $2x + 2y = 9$ where the value of x lies in the range $0 \leqslant x \leqslant 2$

Our First Equation

$4x = y + 3$
$y = 4x - 3$

x	0	1	2
$y = 4x - 3$	(4×0−3=) **-3**	(4×1−3=) **1**	(4×2−3=) **5**

Our Second Equation

$2x + 2y = 9$
$2y = 9 - 2x$
$y = \dfrac{9 - 2x}{2}$

x	0	1	2
$y = \dfrac{9 - 2x}{2}$	$\left(\dfrac{9 - 2\times0}{2}\right)=$ **4.5**	$\left(\dfrac{9 - 2\times1}{2}\right)=$ **3.5**	$\left(\dfrac{9 - 2\times2}{2}\right)=$ **2.5**

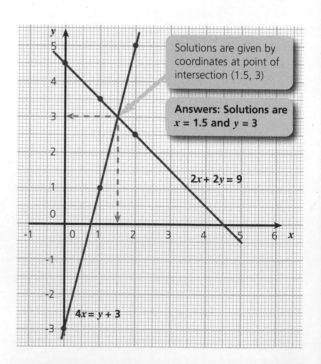

Solutions are given by coordinates at point of intersection (1.5, 3)

Answers: Solutions are $x = 1.5$ and $y = 3$

> To check our solutions substitute $x = 1.5$ and $y = 3$ into our two equations:
> $4x = y + 3$: $4 \times 1.5 = 3 + 3$: $6 = 3 + 3$ ✔
> $2x + 2y = 9$: $2 \times 1.5 + 2 \times 3 = 9$: $3 + 6 = 9$ ✔

Simultaneous Equations

Solving Simultaneous Linear and Quadratic Equations

You are also expected to be able to solve by elimination two simultaneous equations with two unknowns (i.e. x and y), where one equation is linear in each unknown (e.g. $y = 7x - 6$, $2x + y = 11$) and the other equation is linear in one unknown and quadratic in the other (e.g. $y = 3x^2$), or is of the form $x^2 + y^2 = r^2$ (e.g. $x^2 + y^2 = 25$ which is the same as $x^2 + y^2 = 5^2$). $x^2 + y^2 = r^2$ is the equation of a circle of radius r, centred at the origin (0,0).

Examples

1 Solve the two simultaneous equations:
$y = 7x + 6$ and $y = 3x^2$

> Label the equations ① and ②

$$y = 7x + 6 \quad ①$$
$$y = 3x^2 \quad ②$$

> Since both equations have y on its own as the subject, substitute y from equation ② into equation ①. Doing this will remove y from equation ①.

$$3x^2 = 7x + 6$$
$$3x^2 - 7x - 6 = 0$$

> What we have now is a quadratic equation. Always solve by factorisation if possible (see page 32). However you can solve by completing the square or by using the quadratic formula.

$$3x^2 - 7x - 6 = 0$$
$$(x - 3)(3x + 2) = 0$$

And so... $x - 3 = 0$
$$x = 3$$

or... $3x + 2 = 0$
$$x = \frac{-2}{3}$$

> To find the value of y, (when $x = 3$) substitute $x = 3$ into equation ①...

$$y = 7x + 6$$
$$y = (7 \times 3) + 6 = 27$$

One pair of solutions is $x = 3$ and $y = 27$

> To find the value of y (when $x = \frac{-2}{3}$) substitute $x = \frac{-2}{3}$ into equation ① or ②. If we take equation ①...

$$y = 7x + 6$$
$$y = (7 \times \tfrac{-2}{3}) + 6 = 1\tfrac{1}{3}$$

The other pair of solutions is $x = \frac{-2}{3}$ and $y = 1\frac{1}{3}$

> Always check your solutions by substituting them into equation ② since we used equation ① to find them.

2 Solve the two simultaneous equations:
$2x + y = 11$ and $x^2 + y^2 = 25$

> Label the equations ① and ②

$$2x + y = 11 \quad ①$$
$$x^2 + y^2 = 25 \quad ②$$

> Rearrange equation ① to make y the subject.

$$y = 11 - 2x$$

> We can now substitute y from equation ① into equation ②. Doing this will remove y from equation ②.

$$x^2 + (11 - 2x)^2 = 25$$
$$x^2 + (11 - 2x)(11 - 2x) = 25$$
$$x^2 + 121 - 22x - 22x + 4x^2 = 25$$
$$x^2 + 4x^2 - 22x - 22x + 121 - 25 = 0$$
$$5x^2 - 44x + 96 = 0$$
$$(x - 4)(5x - 24) = 0$$

And so... $x - 4 = 0$
$$x = 4$$

or... $5x - 24 = 0$
$$5x = 24$$
$$x = \frac{24}{5} = 4.8$$

> To find the value of y (when $x = 4$) substitute $x = 4$ into rearranged equation ①...

$$y = 11 - 2x$$
$$y = 11 - (2 \times 4) = 3$$

One pair of solutions is $x = 4$ and $y = 3$

> To find the value of y (when $x = 4.8$) substitute $x = 4.8$ into rearranged equation ①...

$$y = 11 - 2x$$
$$y = 11 - (2 \times 4.8) = 1.4$$

The other pair of solutions is $x = 4.8$ and $y = 1.4$

> Always check your solutions by substituting them into equation ② since we used equation ① to find them.

Simultaneous Equations

Solving Simultaneous Linear and Quadratic Equations Graphically

Approximate solutions to simultaneous linear and quadratic equations can also be found graphically. When drawn there are two points of intersection (although there are exceptions) to give us two pairs of solutions.

A* Tip

When solving quadratic and linear equations simultaneously, remember that the point of intersection gives both values to each possible solution of the equations.

Examples

① Solve graphically the two simultaneous equations $y - x = 4$ and $y = 2x^2$ where the value of x lies in the range $-2 \leqslant x \leqslant 2$.

Our First Equation

$y - x = 4$
$\therefore y = x + 4$

x	-2	0	2
$y = x + 4$	2	4	6

Our Second Equation

$y = 2x^2$
(see page 47)

x	-2	-1	0	1	2
$y = 2x^2$	8	2	0	2	8

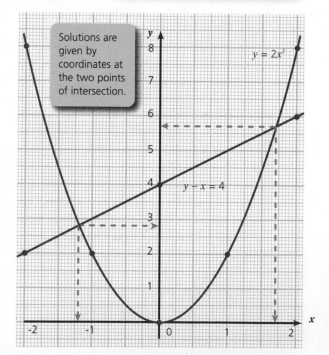

Solutions are given by coordinates at the two points of intersection.

One pair of solutions is $x = -1.2$ and $y = 2.8$
The other pair of solutions is $x = 1.7$ and $y = 5.7$

Remember to check your solutions by substituting the values of x and y into your two equations.

Remember to draw your graphs as accurately as possible. Only approximate solutions can be found.

② Solve graphically the two simultaneous equations $x + y = -1$ and $x^2 + y^2 = 9$ where the value of x lies in the range $-3 \leqslant x \leqslant 3$.

Our First Equation

$x + y = -1$
$\therefore y = -x - 1$

x	-3	0	3
$y = -x - 1$	2	-1	-4

Our Second Equation

The equation is $x^2 + y^2 = 9$ or $x^2 + y^2 = 3^2$, i.e. the equation of a circle of radius 3 units centred at the origin (0,0).

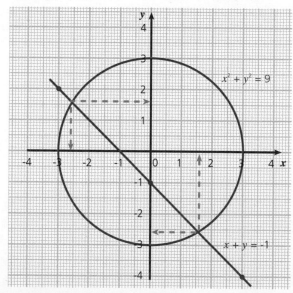

One pair of solutions is $x = -2.6$ and $y = 1.6$
The other pair of solutions is $x = 1.6$ and $y = -2.6$

N.B. It is possible to get only one pair of solutions. This would occur if the line was a tangent to the curve or circle.

Remember to check your solutions by substituting the values of x and y into your two equations.

Graphs of Quadratic Functions

Drawing Graphs of Quadratic Functions

A quadratic function is one that can be put in the form $y = ax^2 + bx + c$. Examples would include $y = x^2$, $y = x^2 - 5$, $y = x^2 - 2x$ and $y = x^2 + 4$. These functions always produce a curved graph such as the ones below. To draw a curved graph we need to plot a **full range of points** as this increases the accuracy of our curve (compare this with straight line graphs).

Notice that all quadratic graphs are symmetric about a line parallel to the y-axis, i.e. a mirror line with equation $x = a\ number$.

Examples

1 Draw the graph of $y = x^2$ for values of x between **-3** and **3** ($-3 \leqslant x \leqslant 3$).

Table of results for $y = x^2$

x	-3	-2	-1	0	1	2	3
$y = x^2$	$(-3)^2=$ 9	$(-2)^2=$ 4	$(-1)^2=$ 1	$(0)^2=$ 0	$(1)^2=$ 1	$(2)^2=$ 4	$(3)^2=$ 9

We now have the coordinates of 7 points, so we can draw our graph.

Remember… Your curve must be smooth and it must pass through all of the points plotted.

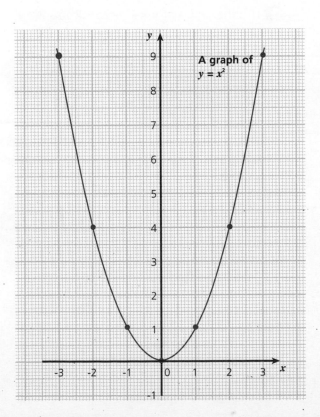

A graph of $y = x^2$

2 Draw the graph of $y = 2x^2 + x - 6$ for values of x between **-3** and **3** ($-3 \leqslant x \leqslant 3$).

Table of results for $y = 2x^2 + x - 6$

x	-3	-2	-1	0	1	2	3
$2x^2$	18	8	2	0	2	8	18
x	-3	-2	-1	0	1	2	3
-6	-6	-6	-6	-6	-6	-6	-6
$y = 2x^2 + x - 6$	9	0	-5	-6	-3	4	15

Again we have the coordinates of 7 points, so we can draw our graph.

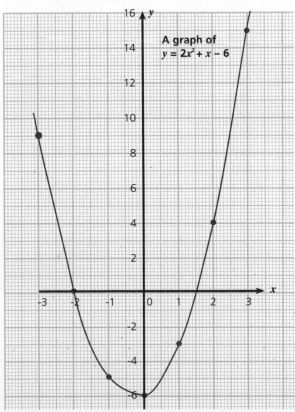

A graph of $y = 2x^2 + x - 6$

Graphs of Quadratic Functions

Solving Quadratic Equations Graphically

Approximate solutions to a quadratic equation can be found from the graph of the corresponding quadratic function.

For example, the graph of $y = x^2 - 2x - 2$ (see page 47) can be used to solve the quadratic equation $x^2 - 2x - 2 = 0$.

| Our quadratic equation is... | $\boxed{x^2 - 2x - 2} = 0$ |
| Our graph is... | $y = \boxed{x^2 - 2x - 2}$ |

Since our quadratic equation corresponds to our quadratic function (i.e. $x^2 - 2x - 2$ is common to both) then approximate solutions are simply the x values where the graph crosses the line $y = 0$, i.e. the x-**axis**.

The two approximate solutions to the equation $x^2 - 2x - 2 = 0$ are $x = -0.7$ and $x = 2.7$.

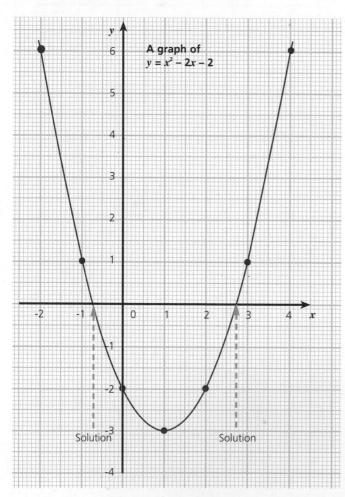

A graph of $y = x^2 - 2x - 2$

A graph of a quadratic function can also be used to solve a wide variety of quadratic equations. However, you will probably have to rearrange the quadratic equation so that it corresponds to the quadratic function before any solutions can be obtained.

Examples

1 Use the graph of $y = x^2 - 2x - 2$ to solve the quadratic equation $x^2 - 2x - 5 = 0$.

Firstly, we need to rearrange the quadratic equation so that it corresponds to the quadratic function.

Our equation is...	$x^2 - 2x - 5 = 0$
Add 3 to both sides	$x^2 - 2x - 5 + 3 = 0 + 3$
Our equation now becomes...	$\boxed{x^2 - 2x - 2} = 3$
Our graph is...	$y = \boxed{x^2 - 2x - 2}$

The solutions are the x values where the graph crosses the line $y = 3$: $x = -1.4$ and $x = 3.4$

A graph of $y = x^2 - 2x - 2$

2 Use the graph of $y = x^2 - 2x - 2$ to solve the quadratic equation $x^2 - 2x - 1 = 0$.

Our equation is...	$x^2 - 2x - 1 = 0$
Subtract 1 from both sides	$x^2 - 2x - 1 - 1 = 0 - 1$
Our equation now becomes...	$\boxed{x^2 - 2x - 2} = -1$
Our graph is...	$y = \boxed{x^2 - 2x - 2}$

This time the solutions are the x values where the graph crosses the line $y = -1$: $x = -0.4$ and $x = 2.4$

A graph of $y = x^2 - 2x - 2$

Graphs of Simple Cubic Functions

A cubic function is one that can be put in the form $y = ax^3 + bx^2 + cx + d$. Examples would include $y = x^3$, $y = x^3 + 1$ and $y = 2x^3$. These functions always produce a curved graph with a double bend in it such as the one below. Again we need to plot a full range of points as this increases the accuracy of our curve.

For example, draw the graph of $y = x^3$ for values of x between **-3** and **3** ($-3 \leqslant x \leqslant 3$).

Table of results for $y = x^3$							
x	-3	-2	-1	0	1	2	3
$y = x^3$	$(-3)^3=$ -27	$(-2)^3=$ -8	$(-1)^3=$ -1	$(0)^3=$ 0	$(1)^3=$ 1	$(2)^3=$ 8	$(3)^3=$ 27

Since we now have the coordinates of 7 points we can draw our graph. As before, your curve must be smooth and it must pass through all of the points plotted.

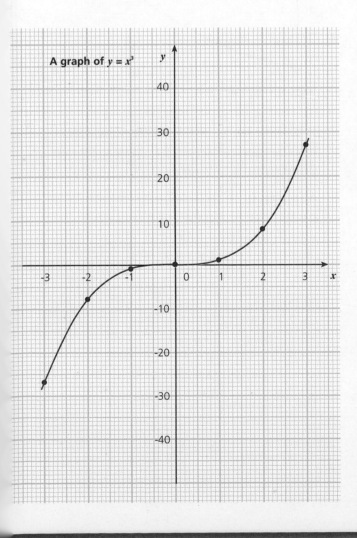

A graph of $y = x^3$

Graph of the Reciprocal Function

$$y = \frac{1}{x} \text{ with } x \neq 0$$

The reciprocal function $y = \frac{1}{x}$ with $x \neq 0$ gives us two separate curves.

For negative values of x								
x	-5	-4	-3	-2	-1	-0.5	-0.$\dot{3}$	-0.25	-0.2
$y = \frac{1}{x}$	-0.2	-0.25	-0.$\dot{3}$	-0.5	-1	-2	-3	-4	-5

For positive values of x								
x	0.2	0.25	0.$\dot{3}$	0.5	1	2	3	4	5
$y = \frac{1}{x}$	5	4	3	2	1	0.5	0.$\dot{3}$	0.25	0.2

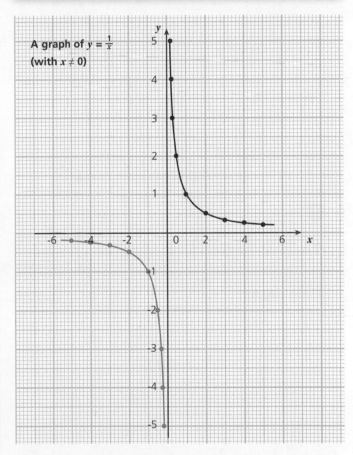

A graph of $y = \frac{1}{x}$
(with $x \neq 0$)

With the function $y = \frac{1}{x}$, for any point on either curve the x coordinate multiplied by the y coordinate always equals 1.

e.g. When $x = -2$, $y = -0.5...$
to give us $x \times y = -2 \times -0.5 = 1$
When $x = 0.25$, $y = 4...$
to give us $x \times y = 0.25 \times 4 = 1$

Graphs of Other Functions

Graphs of the Exponential Function
$y = k^x$

You need to be able to draw the graph of the exponential function $y = k^x$ for integer values of x and simple positive values of k.

Examples

1 $y = k^x$ where $k > 1$, e.g. $y = 2^x$

x	0	1	2	3	4
$y = 2^x$	$(2)^0 =$ **1**	$(2)^1 =$ **2**	$(2)^2 =$ **4**	$(2)^3 =$ **8**	$(2)^4 =$ **16**

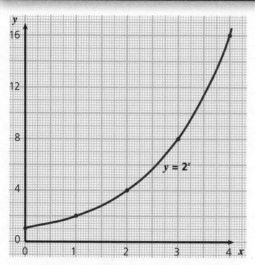

2 $y = k^x$ where $0 < k < 1$, e.g. $y = (0.5)^x$

x	0	1	2	3	4
$y = (0.5)^x$	$(0.5)^0 =$ **1**	$(0.5)^1 =$ **0.5**	$(0.5)^2 =$ **0.25**	$(0.5)^3 =$ **0.125**	$(0.5)^4 =$ **0.0625**

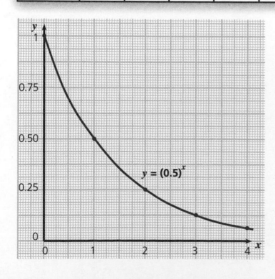

3 The graph below is known to fit the relationship $y = ab^x$. Use the graph to find the value of a and b and the relationship.

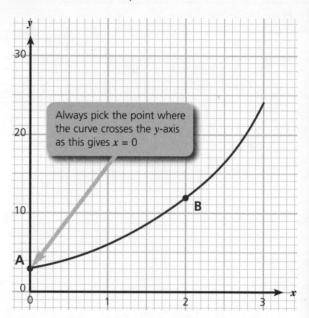

> Always pick the point where the curve crosses the y-axis as this gives $x = 0$

This time we need to take values for x and y from our graph and then substitute them into the relationship, $y = ab^x$.

At point A:
$x = 0$ (curve crosses the y-axis) and $y = 3$
$y = ab^x$ gives us: $3 = ab^0$
$$3 = a \times 1$$

> Anything to the power of $0 = 1$

and so… $a = 3$

At point B:
$x = 2$ and $y = 12$ (we know that $a = 3$)
$y = ab^x$ gives us: $12 = 3b^2$
$$4 = b^2$$
and so… $b = \sqrt{4} = 2$

The relationship is: $y = 3 \times 2^x$

Graphs of Other Functions

Graph of $y = \sin x$

If we plot the graph of $y = \sin x$ for values of x from $0°$ to $360°$ we get the following:

$x(°)$	0	30	60	90	120	150	180	210	240	270	300	330	360
$y = \sin x$	0	0.5	0.87	1	0.87	0.5	0	-0.5	-0.87	-1	-0.87	-0.5	0

The graph is wave-like, where the maximum value of $\sin x$ is **1** when $x = 90°$ and the minimum value of $\sin x$ is **-1** when $x = 270°$. When $x = 0°$, **180°** or **360°** the graph crosses the x-axis and $\sin x$ is equal to **0**.

The graph above is for values of x from $0°$ to $360°$. It is also possible to extend beyond this range, i.e. values of x less than $0°$ and greater than $360°$. The pattern or cycle repeats itself every $360°$, as shown in the graph below.

Graph of $y = \cos x$

If we plot the graph of $y = \cos x$ for values of x from $0°$ to $360°$ we get the following:

$x(°)$	0	30	60	90	120	150	180	210	240	270	300	330	360
$y = \cos x$	1	0.87	0.5	0	-0.5	-0.87	-1	-0.87	-0.5	0	0.5	0.87	1

The graph is wave-like (same as the graph of $y = \sin x$, except that it has been shifted 90° to the left), where the maximum value of **cos**x is **1** when $x = 0°$ or **360°** and the minimum value of **cos**x is **-1** when $x = 180°$. When $x = 90°$ or **270°** the graph crosses the x-axis and **cos**x is equal to **0**.

Also, as for the graph of $y = \sin x$, we can extend beyond $0°$ and $360°$. The pattern repeats itself every $360°$.

Graph of $y = \tan x$

If we plot the graph of $y = \tan x$ for values of x from $0°$ to $360°$ we get the following:

$x(°)$	0	30	60	90	120	150	180	210	240	270	300	330	360
$y = \tan x$	0	0.58	1.73	INT	-1.73	-0.58	0	0.58	1.73	INT	-1.73	-0.58	0

The graph is not wave-like like the $\sin x$ or $\cos x$ graphs. When $x = 90°$ or **270°** then **tan**x is undefined. When $x = 0°$, **180°** or **360°** the graph crosses the x-axis and **tan**x is equal to **0**.

Also, we can extend beyond $0°$ and $360°$. The pattern repeats itself every **180°**.

Transformation of Functions

Four Standard Transformations

If $y =$ **an expression involving** x then we can say that y is a function of x or $y = f(x)$. You may well be asked to draw the graph of another function, which is related to the graph of a function that has been already drawn for you.

Examples

1 $y = af(x)$... graph is **stretched** in the y direction

If $a > 1$, e.g. $y = 2x^2$, then all the points are stretched upwards in the y direction by a factor of a (opposite $a = 2$)

If $a < 1$, e.g. $y = 0.5x^2$, then all the points are moved a times their distance from the x-axis. The stretch factor is 0.5 in this case (opposite $a = 0.5$)

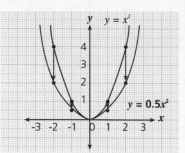

2 $y = f(ax)$... graph is **stretched** in the x direction

If $a > 1$, e.g. $y = (2x)^2$, then all the points are stretched inwards in the x direction by a factor of $\frac{1}{a}$ (opposite $\frac{1}{a} = \frac{1}{2} = 0.5$)

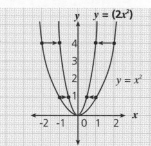

If $a < 1$, e.g. $y = (0.5x)^2$, then all the points are stretched outwards in the x direction by a factor of $\frac{1}{a}$ (opposite $\frac{1}{a} = \frac{1}{0.5} = 2$)

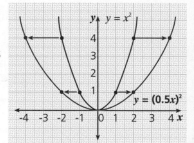

3 $y = f(x + a)$... graph is **translated** in the x direction

If a **is positive**, e.g. $y = (x + 1)^2$, then all the points are translated to the left by the value of a (opposite $a = 1$)

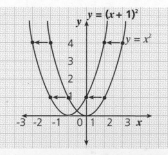

If a **is negative**, e.g. $y = (x - 1)^2$, then all the points are translated to the right by the value of a (opposite $a = -1$)

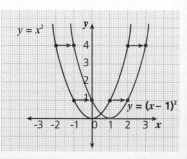

4 $y = f(x) + a$... graph is **translated** in the y direction

If a **is positive**, e.g. $y = x^2 + 1$, then all the points are translated upwards by the value of a (opposite $a = 1$)

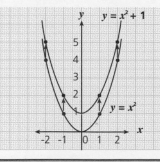

If a **is negative**, e.g. $y = x^2 - 1$, then all the points are translated downwards by the value of a (opposite $a = -1$)

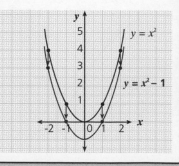

Real Life Graphs

xy

Conversion Graphs

Conversion graphs are used to convert values of one unit into another, e.g. pounds sterling (£) into dollars ($) or any other currency, miles into kilometres, etc.

Example

Draw a conversion graph for pounds sterling and dollars up to £30 if £1 = $1.60. From your graph convert…

a) £170 into dollars

b) $400 into pounds sterling.

Before we can draw our graph we need a table of values for pounds sterling and dollars.

Pounds Sterling (£)	Dollars ($)
100	(100 × 1.6 =) 160
200	(200 × 1.6 =) 320
300	(300 × 1.6 =) 480

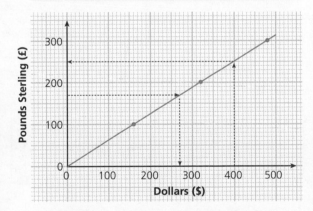

a) Go to £170 on the pounds sterling axis, draw a dotted line across (➡) to the graph and then down (⬇) to the dollars axis. **£170 = $270**

b) Go to $400 on the dollars axis, draw a dotted line up (⬆) to the graph and then across (⬅) to the pounds sterling axis. **$400 = £250**

Graphs that Describe Real Life Situations

Here are six examples (there are numerous others) where a graph can be used to show a real life situation.

All of these graphs require common sense in their interpretation as each one is very different.

Examples

1 Temperature at different times of day

2 Weight of a man as he gets older

3 Value of a car as it gets older

4 Pulse rate of a runner after the race is over

5 Height of a girl as she gets older

6 Temperature of a thermostatically controlled room over a period of time

Direct and Inverse Proportion

Direct Proportion

Two quantities are in direct proportion if when we double (or treble) one of the quantities then the other quantity also doubles (or trebles). If two quantities y and x are in direct proportion then a graph of values of y against values of x would be a straight line.

$$\text{gradient} = \frac{y \text{ change}}{x \text{ change}}$$

We can say that...

y is directly proportional to x or $y \propto x$ which means that $y = kx$ where k is a constant, i.e. a number that doesn't change and is given by the **gradient** of the graph.

It is also possible for $y \propto x^2$, $y \propto x^3$ and so on.

Example

The distance, d, travelled by an accelerating car which was initially stationary is directly proportional to the **square** of the time, t, of travel. The table below gives values of d and t. What is the relationship between d and t?

$t(s)$	0	1	2	3
$t^2(s)$	$(0^2=)\ 0$	$(1^2=)\ 1$	$(2^2=)\ 4$	$(3^2=)\ 9$
$d(m)$	0	3	12	27

Since $d \propto t^2$ or $d = kt^2$ we've added one row, t^2, to our table (in orange). A graph of d against t^2 will give us a straight line.

$$\begin{aligned}
\text{gradient} &= k \\
&= \frac{d \text{ change}}{t^2 \text{ change}} \\
&= \frac{(27-12)}{(9-4)} \\
&= \frac{15}{5}. \\
&= 3
\end{aligned}$$

Relationship is $d = 3t^2$

Inverse Proportion

Two quantities are in inverse proportion if when we double (or treble) one of the quantities then the other quantity halves (or becomes a third). If two quantities y and x are in inverse proportion then a graph of values of y against values of $\frac{1}{x}$ would be a straight line.

$$\text{gradient} = \frac{y \text{ change}}{\frac{1}{x} \text{ change}}$$

We can say that...

y is inversely proportional to x or $y \propto \frac{1}{x}$ which means that $y = \frac{k}{x}$ where k is a constant and is given by the gradient of the graph.

It is also possible for $y \propto \frac{1}{x^2}$, $y \propto \frac{1}{x^3}$ and so on.

Example

The density, d, of objects of fixed mass is inversely proportional to their volume, V. The table below gives values of d and V. What is the relationship between d and V?

$V(m^3)$	10	5	2	1
$\frac{1}{V}(m^{-3})$	$(\frac{1}{10}=)\ 0.1$	$(\frac{1}{5}=)\ 0.2$	$(\frac{1}{2}=)\ 0.5$	$(\frac{1}{1}=)\ 1$
$d(kg/m^3)$	1	2	5	10

Since $d \propto \frac{1}{V}$ or $d = \frac{k}{V}$ we've added one row, $\frac{1}{V}$, to our table (in orange). A graph of d against $\frac{1}{V}$ will give us a straight line.

$$\begin{aligned}
\text{gradient} &= k \\
&= \frac{d \text{ change}}{\frac{1}{V} \text{ change}} \\
&= \frac{(10-5)}{(1-0.5)} \\
&= \frac{5}{0.5} \\
&= 10
\end{aligned}$$

Relationship is $d = \frac{10}{V}$

Angles

Acute, Right, Obtuse and Reflex Angles

All angles are measured in **degrees** (°). A protractor can be used to measure the size of an angle.

An angle less than 90° is called an **acute angle**.

An angle equal to 90° is called a **right angle**.

An angle greater than 90° but less than 180° is called an **obtuse angle**.

An angle greater than 180° is called a **reflex angle**.

Adjacent Angles and Angles at a Point

Angles on a straight line add up to 180° (also known as adjacent angles).

$a = 120°$
$b = 60°$ $a + b = 180°$

$p = 45°$
$q = 90°$ $p + q + r = 180°$
$r = 45°$

Angles at a point add up to 360°.

$a = 240°$
$b = 120°$ $a + b = 360°$

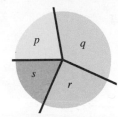

$p = 80°$
$q = 125°$
$r = 90°$ $p + q + r + s = 360°$
$s = 65°$

Vertically opposite angles are equal.

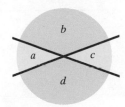

$a = 40°$
$c = 40°$ $\}$ Vertically opposite
$b = 140°$
$d = 140°$ $\}$ Vertically opposite

Examples

1 Work out the angles *a* and *b*

$a = 180° - 30° = 150°$
(Angles on a straight line add up to 180°)
$b = 30°$ (Vertically opposite angles are equal)

2 Work out the angle *c*

$c = 360° - (120° + 160°)$
$c = 360° - 280° = 80°$
(Angles at a point add up to 360°)

Angles

Parallel Lines

Parallel lines run in exactly the same direction and never meet. Parallel lines are shown by arrows. There is no limit to the number of lines that may run parallel to each other. When a straight line crosses two or more parallel lines, corresponding, alternate and allied angles are formed.

Alternate Angles and Corresponding Angles

- Alternate angles are formed on opposite (alternate) sides of a line that crosses two or more parallel lines.
- Alternate angles are always equal in size.
- Alternate angles can be easily spotted because they form a letter Z (although sometimes it may be reversed Σ).

Examples

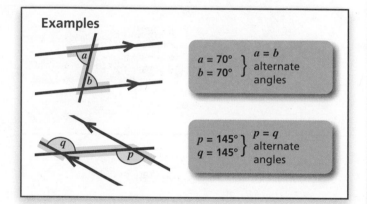

$a = 70°$
$b = 70°$ } $a = b$ alternate angles

$p = 145°$
$q = 145°$ } $p = q$ alternate angles

- Corresponding angles are formed on the same side of a line, that crosses two or more parallel lines. They all appear in matching (corresponding) positions above or below the parallel lines.
- Corresponding angles are always equal in size.
- Corresponding angles can be easily spotted because they form a letter F (although sometimes it may be reversed, ꟻ, or upside down ⅎ, ⅃).

Examples

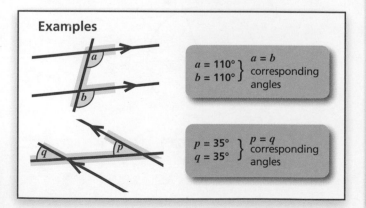

$a = 110°$
$b = 110°$ } $a = b$ corresponding angles

$p = 35°$
$q = 35°$ } $p = q$ corresponding angles

Angle Proofs

The diagram shows triangle ABC with the side AC extended to D and CE drawn parallel to AB.

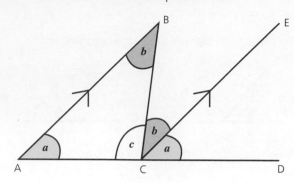

- The two angles labelled a are equal as they are corresponding angles.
- The two angles labelled b are equal as they are alternate angles.
- At point C angles a, b and c lie on the straight line ACD, so $a + b + c = 180°$.

> This proves that the sum of the angles of a triangle is 180°

- Angle BCD is an exterior angle of the triangle. **Angle BCD = $a + b$**
- The interior angles opposite to C are a and b.

> This proves that the exterior angle of a triangle is equal to the sum of the two interior opposite angles.

Example
Find angle r

To find r you should draw a 3rd parallel line through r.

Using alternate angles, the top part of $r = 28°$, lower part = 33°
∴ $r = 61°$

Angles of Polygons

Interior Angles of a Polygon

The diagram shows a pentagon ABCDE divided into three triangles.

The angles inside each triangle add up to 180° and these combine to make the interior angles of the pentagon.

Therefore, the sum of the interior angles of a pentagon is **3 × 180° = 540°**.

A hexagon may be divided into four triangles in the same way.

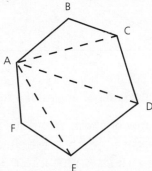

Therefore, the sum of the interior angles of a hexagon is **4 × 180° = 720°**.

In general, a polygon with n sides may be divided into $(n − 2)$ triangles.

Therefore, the sum of the interior angles of an n-sided polygon is **$(n − 2) × 180°$**.

> ### Example
> The sum of the interior angles of a polygon is 3240°. How many sides does it have?
>
> $$(n − 2) × 180 = 3240$$
> $$n − 2 = \frac{3240}{180}$$
> $$n − 2 = 18$$
> $$n = 20$$
>
> The polygon has **20 sides**.

Interior and Exterior Angles

An exterior angle is formed by extending one side of a polygon. In the diagram, the side DE is extended to F.

Angle AED is an interior angle.
Angle AEF is an exterior angle.

The interior and exterior angles at a vertex always make a straight line and always add up to 180°.

The sum of all of the exterior angles of a polygon is always 360°.

Regular Polygons

Regular polygons have…
- all sides of the same length
- all interior angles of the same size
- all exterior angles of the same size

> ### Example
> Calculate the size of **a)** each exterior, and **b)** each interior angle for a regular hexagon (6 sides).
>
>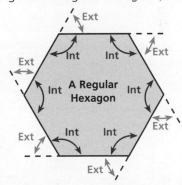
>
> A regular hexagon has 6 equal interior angles and 6 equal exterior angles.
> **a)** The exterior angles of a hexagon add up to 360°
>
> Each exterior angle = $\frac{360°}{6}$ **= 60°**
>
> **b)** The interior angle + the exterior angle add up to 180°
>
> Each interior angle = 180° − exterior angle
> $$= 180° − 60°$$
> **$= 120°$**

Quadrilaterals

Types of Quadrilateral

A quadrilateral is a 4-sided, two-dimensional shape, which has interior angles that add up to 360°.

Square
- All the sides are equal in length
- Opposite sides are parallel
- All the angles are equal to 90°
- Diagonals are equal and bisect each other at right-angles.
- Diagonals also bisect each of the interior angles.

Parallelogram
- Opposite sides are equal in length
- Opposite sides are parallel
- Opposite angles are equal in size
- Diagonals bisect each other.

Rhombus
- All the sides are equal in length
- Opposite sides are parallel
- Opposite angles are equal in size
- Diagonals bisect each other at right-angles
- Diagonals also bisect the interior angles.

Rectangle
- Opposite sides are equal in length
- Opposite sides are parallel
- All the angles are equal to 90°
- Diagonals are equal and bisect each other.

Trapezium
- No sides equal in length
- One pair of sides parallel
- No angles equal in size.

Kite
- 2 pairs of equal adjacent sides
- 1 pair of opposite equal angles
- Diagonals cross at right-angles and one bisects the other.

> Bisect means to divide into two equal parts.

The Interior Angles of a Quadrilateral

In this quadrilateral...

$a = 63°, b = 106°, c = 145°, d = 46°$

If we add these together...

$63° + 106° + 145° + 46° = 360°$

The sum of four angles in a quadrilateral willl always equal 360° and can be proved by dividing the quadrilateral into two triangles.

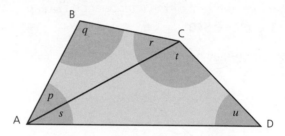

$p + q + r = 180°$ (Interior angles of a triangle)
$s + t + u = 180°$ (Interior angles of a triangle)

The sum of the interior angles of the quadrilateral is $(p + s) + q + (r + t) + u$ which is, therefore, equal to $(p + q + r) + (s + t + u)$, i.e. $180° + 180° = 360°$

Example

Without measuring, work out the size of the angle marked x.

PQ is parallel to RS and PS is parallel to QR. $PQRS$ could be either a parallelogram or a rhombus. In both types of quadrilateral the opposite angles are equal.

$$55° + 55° + x + x = 360°$$
$$110° + 2x = 360°$$
$$2x = 360° - 110°$$
$$2x = 250°$$
$$\boldsymbol{x = 125°}$$

Symmetry

Line or Reflective Symmetry

A two-dimensional shape has a **line of symmetry** if it can be 'cut in half' so that one half of the shape is an exact mirror image of the other half of the shape.

It is possible for shapes to have more than 1 line of symmetry. The shape below can be 'cut in half' more than once.

A simple way to find lines of symmetry is to use tracing paper. Draw in where you think the line of symmetry is and trace one side of your shape carefully on the tracing paper. Then flip the tracing paper over about the line of symmetry. If your line of symmetry is correct you should get an exact mirror image.

Some shapes, especially regular polygons (see page 57) can have more lines of symmetry. However, there are shapes that have **no line of symmetry**. The shapes below cannot be 'cut in half' to give exact mirror images.

Rotational Symmetry

A two-dimensional shape has **rotational symmetry** if it can be 'rotated about a point', called the centre of rotation, to a different position where it looks the same as it was to begin with. The order of rotational symmetry is equal to the number of times a shape fits onto itself in one 360° turn.

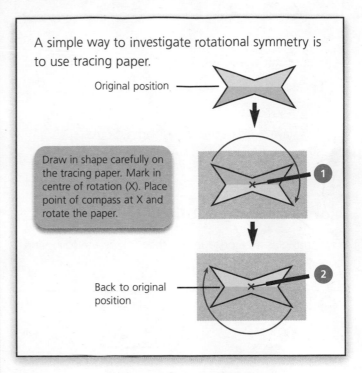

A simple way to investigate rotational symmetry is to use tracing paper.

Original position

Draw in shape carefully on the tracing paper. Mark in centre of rotation (X). Place point of compass at X and rotate the paper.

Back to original position

The following shape has rotational symmetry of order 3.

Some shapes, especially regular polygons can have rotational symmetry of even higher orders. However, there are shapes that have **rotational symmetry of order 1** (this can also be referred to as **no rotational symmetry**). These shapes only look the same as their original position when they have been rotated one complete turn (360°).

Congruence and Similiarity

Congruent Figures

Congruent figures have the same shape and size.

> **Example**
>
>
>
> Figure ABCD and figure PQRS are congruent because $\hat{A} = \hat{P}$, $\hat{B} = \hat{Q}$, $\hat{C} = \hat{R}$ and $\hat{D} = \hat{S}$.
>
> Two congruent figures have angles the same size and have sides of the same length. So AB = PQ, BC = QR, CD = RS and DA = SP.

Congruent Triangles

Two triangles are congruent if they satisfy the following conditions:

1 **Three Sides, SSS** AB = PQ BC = QR AC = PR ∴ ABC and PQR are congruent triangles.	
2 **Two Sides and Included Angle, SAS** AB = PQ AC = PR $\hat{A} = \hat{P}$ ∴ ABC and PQR are congruent triangles.	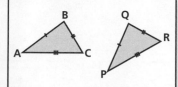
3 **Two Angles and One Corresponding Side, ASA** AB = PQ $\hat{A} = \hat{P}$ $\hat{B} = \hat{Q}$ ∴ ABC and PQR are congruent triangles.	 **N.B.** In our diagram we've used AB = PQ. However we could have used BC = QR or AC = PR. The two triangles are still congruent.
4 **Right Angle, Hypotenuse and One Other Side, RHS** AB = PQ BC = QR $\hat{C} = \hat{R} = 90°$ ∴ ABC and PQR are congruent triangles.	 **N.B.** In our diagram we've used BC = QR. However we could have used AC = PR. The two triangles would still be congruent.

Similar Figures

Similar figures have the same shape, but may be different in size.

When comparing similar figures, lengths of corresponding sides are in the same ratio.

> **Example**
> The two triangles below are similar.
>
> Calculate the length of…
>
> **a)** QR
>
> **b)** AC
>
>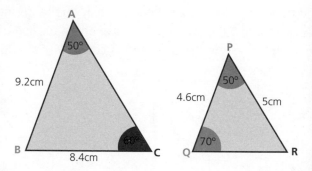
>
> In triangle ABC, $\hat{B} = 70°$ (180° − (60° + 50°)) and in triangle PQR, $\hat{R} = 60°$ (180° − (70° + 50°))
>
> And so $\hat{A} = \hat{P}$, $\hat{B} = \hat{Q}$, $\hat{C} = \hat{R}$
>
> This means that triangle ABC is similar to triangle PQR which means that…
>
> $$\frac{AB}{PQ} = \frac{BC}{QR} = \frac{AC}{PR}$$
>
> > Don't assume that the shapes (in this case triangles) are always lettered in alphabetical order
>
> $$\frac{9.2cm}{4.6cm} = \frac{8.4cm}{QR} = \frac{AC}{5cm}$$
>
> We can now calculate the unknown lengths. One method is to rearrange the equations above to find QR and AC, but in this case the larger triangle simply has twice the dimensions of the smaller one.
>
> **a)** $QR = \dfrac{8.4cm \times 4.6cm}{9.2} = 4.2cm$ or $\dfrac{8.4}{2} = 4.2cm$
>
> **b)** $AC = \dfrac{9.2cm \times 5cm}{4.6} = 10cm$ or 5 × 2 = 10cm

Pythagoras' Theorem

Pythagoras

Pythagoras' theorem states that in any right-angled triangle, the square on the hypotenuse is equal to the sum of the squares on the other two sides.

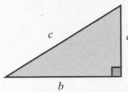

The theorem may be written in algebra as $c^2 = a^2 + b^2$. You can rearrange this to calculate one of the shorter sides, e.g. $a^2 = c^2 - b^2$.

Examples

1 Calculate the length of c in the following right-angled triangle to (1 d.p).

b = 3.4cm

This triangle is not to scale.

a = 4.6cm

c

Using Pythagoras' theorem
$c^2 = a^2 + b^2$
$c^2 = 4.6^2 + 3.4^2$
$c^2 = 21.16 + 11.56$
$c^2 = 32.72$

To get c we need to take the square root.

$c = \sqrt{32.72}$
$c = \textbf{5.7cm}$

2 Calculate the height of the isosceles triangle (to 3 s.f.).

c = 6cm   6cm

a

b = 2cm

4cm

First we must divide the triangle into two right-angled triangles (as shown by the dotted line) in order to use Pythagoras' theorem. Label the one we are going to work with (in red).

$a^2 = c^2 - b^2$ ← This would be true for either right-angled triangle
$a^2 = 6^2 - 2^2$
$a^2 = 36 - 4$ ← Half the base of isosceles triangle
$a^2 = 32$
$a = \sqrt{32}$ ← To get a we need to take the square root
$= \textbf{5.66cm}$

Pythagoras' Theorem in 3-D

Pythagoras' theorem may be adapted to work in three dimensions.

The diagram shows a cuboid with edges of length a, b and c.

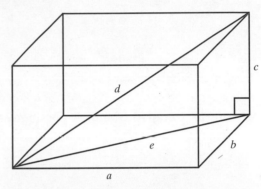

The length of one diagonal is d where $d^2 = e^2 + c^2$
But, $e^2 = a^2 + b^2$ so, $d^2 = a^2 + b^2 + c^2$

Example

Calculate the length of the red diagonal shown (to 1 d.p.).

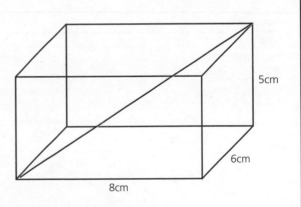

5cm

6cm

8cm

Using $d^2 = a^2 + b^2 + c^2$
$d^2 = 8^2 + 6^2 + 5^2$
$d^2 = 125$
$d = \sqrt{125} = 11.18...$

The length of the diagonal is **11.2cm**

Trigonometry

Calculating the Length of an Unknown Side

In this form, the three triganometrical ratios – sine, cosine and tangent – can be used to calculate unknown sides and angles in **right-angled triangles**. The formula triangles make it easy to rearrange each ratio as required.

$\sin\theta = \dfrac{opp}{hyp}$ $opp = \sin\theta \times hyp$ $hyp = \dfrac{opp}{\sin\theta}$

$\cos\theta = \dfrac{adj}{hyp}$ $adj = \cos\theta \times hyp$ $hyp = \dfrac{adj}{\cos\theta}$

$\tan\theta = \dfrac{opp}{adj}$ $opp = \tan\theta \times adj$ $adj = \dfrac{opp}{\tan\theta}$

A* Tip

Learn the trigonometry ratios as they will not be provided on the formula sheet in the exam.

Examples

1 Calculate the length of BC in the following triangle (to 1 d.p.)

$opp = \sin\theta \times hyp$
$BC = \sin40° \times 10cm$
$BC = 0.643 \times 10cm$
$BC = 6.4cm$

---

2 Calculate the length of AB in the following triangle.

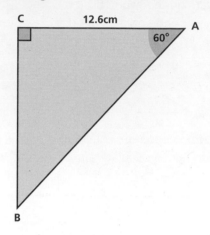

$hyp = \dfrac{adj}{\cos\theta}$

$AB = \dfrac{12.6cm}{\cos60°}$

$AB = \dfrac{12.6}{0.5}$

$AB = 25.2cm$

3 A ladder leans against a vertical wall. The foot of the ladder is 1.6m from the wall and the ladder makes an angle of 30° with the wall. Calculate the height of the wall (to 1 d.p.).

$adj = \dfrac{opp}{\tan\theta}$

$adj = \dfrac{1.6m}{\tan30°}$

$adj = \dfrac{1.6}{0.577}$

height of wall = 2.8m

Trigonometry

Calculating the Size of an Unknown Angle

Example

Calculate the size of angle BAC in the following triangle.

12cm

A   6cm   C

$$\cos\theta = \frac{adj}{hyp}$$

$$\cos B\hat{A}C = \frac{6cm}{12cm}$$

$$\cos B\hat{A}C = 0.5$$

$$B\hat{A}C = \cos^{-1}(0.5)$$

$B\hat{A}C = 60°$

> There is no need to use a formula triangle to calculate the size of an unknown angle. However you still need to remember 'SOH CAH TOA'

> To calculate $B\hat{A}C$ we now have to use the **inverse** cos button on our calculator, i.e. the $\cos^{-1}$ button to get the answer. Ensure your calculator is in 'degree (D)' mode.

A* Tip

You need to become confident at re-arranging formulae when working with more complex trigonometry equations.

Angles of Elevation and Depression

Angles of elevation and depression are both measured from the horizontal direction either upwards or downwards.

A child looking up at an adult…

Horizontal

Angle of elevation

An adult looking down at a child…

Horizontal

Angle of depression

These two angles will always be equal.

Example

The tree in the diagram below is 9m high.

Calculate the angle of elevation to the top of the tree from a point on the ground 20m from the foot of the tree (to 1 d.p.).

9m

θ

20m

$$\tan\theta = \frac{opp}{adj}$$

$$\tan\theta = \frac{9m}{20m}$$

$$\tan\theta = 0.45$$

$$\theta = \tan^{-1}(0.45)$$

> To calculate the angle of elevation θ, we now have to use the inverse tan button on our calculator, i.e. the $\tan^{-1}$ button to get the answer

Angle of elevation = 24.2°

A* Tip

Sin, cos and tan mean nothing by themselves, so make sure they are linked with an angle.

Trigonometry

The Sine Rule

The sine rule can be used in **any** triangle to calculate the length of an unknown side or the size of an unknown angle.

$$\frac{a}{\sin A} = \frac{b}{\sin B} = \frac{c}{\sin C}$$

where a, b and c are the sides opposite angles A, B and C respectively.

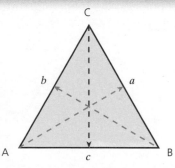

You can only use two parts of the sine rule at any one time:

$$\frac{a}{\sin A} = \frac{b}{\sin B} \quad \textbf{or} \quad \frac{a}{\sin A} = \frac{c}{\sin C} \quad \textbf{or} \quad \frac{b}{\sin B} = \frac{c}{\sin C}$$

The sine rule can be used to calculate…

- the length of an unknown side if we are given the length of one other side and the size of two angles.
- the size of an unknown angle if we are given the length of any two sides and the size of an angle opposite one of these sides.

N.B. The sine rule can be used to solve problems in 2-D or 3-D. It can also be used with right-angled triangles, but you should always use the three trigonometry ratios – sin, cos and tan – because they are a lot easier.

A* Tip

If you know the radius and chord length of a circle, you will need to use trigonometry to find the angle of a sector.

Examples

1 Calculate the length of AB in the following triangle (to 2 d.p.).

Using the sine rule…

$$\frac{a}{\sin A} = \left[\frac{b}{\sin B}\right] \text{ or } = \frac{c}{\sin C}$$

> Since b and sin B play no part in the question, ignore them

$$\therefore \frac{10\text{cm}}{\sin 70°} = \frac{c}{\sin 60°}$$

Rearranging gives us…

$$c = \frac{10 \times \sin 60°}{\sin 70°}$$

$$c = 9.22\text{cm}$$

$$\therefore \text{Length of AB} = \textbf{9.22cm}$$

2 Calculate $\hat{ABC}$ in the following triangle (to 1 d.p.).

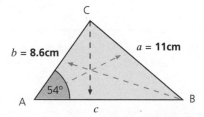

Using the sine rule…

$$\frac{a}{\sin A} = \frac{b}{\sin B} \text{ or } = \left[\frac{c}{\sin C}\right]$$

> Since c and sin C play no part in the question, ignore them

$$\therefore \frac{11\text{cm}}{\sin 54°} = \frac{8.6\text{cm}}{\sin B}$$

Rearranging gives us…

$$\sin B = \frac{8.6 \times \sin 54°}{11} = 0.6325$$

$$\hat{ABC} = \sin^{-1}(0.6325) = 39.23°$$

$$\therefore \text{Size of } \hat{ABC} = \textbf{39.2°}$$

Trigonometry

The Cosine Rule

The cosine rule, like the sine rule, can be used in **any** triangle to calculate the length of an unknown side or the size of an unknown angle.

To find the size of an unknown **side**:

$$a^2 = b^2 + c^2 - 2bc \cos A$$

So, if we wanted to find the length of b or c then the formula becomes:

- $b^2 = a^2 + c^2 - 2ac \cos B$
- $c^2 = a^2 + b^2 - 2ab \cos C$

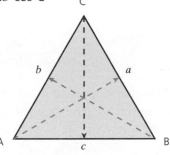

We rearrange the formula to find the size of an unknown **angle**:

- $\cos A = \dfrac{b^2 + c^2 - a^2}{2bc}$

For angles B and C it becomes:

- $\cos B = \dfrac{a^2 + c^2 - b^2}{2ac}$

- $\cos C = \dfrac{a^2 + b^2 - c^2}{2ab}$

The cosine rule (compare to the sine rule) can be used to calculate…

- the length of an unknown side if we are given the length of two sides and the size of their included angle
- the size of an unknown angle if we are given the length of all three sides.

N.B. Like the sine rule, the cosine rule can be used to solve problems in 2-D or 3-D. It can also be used with right-angled triangles, but you should always use the three trigonometry ratios – sin, cos and tan – because they are a lot easier.

Examples

1 Calculate the length of BC in the following triangle (to 2 d.p.).

Using the cosine rule:
$$a^2 = b^2 + c^2 - 2bc \cos A$$
$$= 10^2 + 12^2 - (2 \times 10 \times 12 \times \cos 60°)$$
$$= 100 + 144 - (2 \times 10 \times 12 \times 0.5)$$
$$= 100 + 144 - 120$$
$$= 124$$
$$a = \sqrt{124} = 11.14\text{cm}$$
∴ Length of **BC = 11.14cm**

2 Calculate the size of BÂC in the following triangle (to 2 d.p.).

Using the cosine rule (rearranged):

$$\cos A = \frac{b^2 + c^2 - a^2}{2bc}$$

$$= \frac{9.1^2 + 7.6^2 - 8.4^2}{2 \times 9.1 \times 7.6}$$

$$= \frac{82.81 + 57.76 - 70.56}{138.32}$$

$\cos A = 0.5061$
BÂC $= \cos^{-1} (0.5061) = 59.60°$
∴ size of **BÂC = 59.60°**

Circles

Circles

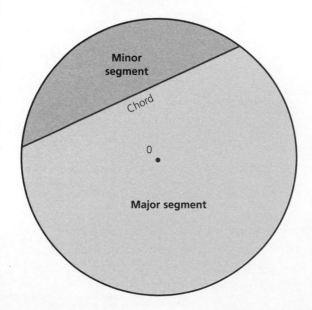

Chords, Tangents and Radii

There are several useful properties relating to chords and tangents of circles. You need to understand the first two of these on this page, but you must understand and be able to explain the third.

1 Tangent and Radius

A tangent is a straight line that touches the circumference of a circle. A tangent at any point on a circle is perpendicular to the radius at that point.

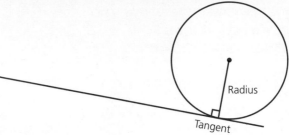

2 Two External Tangents

Tangents from an external point are equal in length, **PQ = PR**. This produces a symmetrical situation in which there are two congruent, right-angled triangles, PQO and PRO.

3 Perpendicular to a Chord

A chord is a straight line joining two points on the circumference, which does not pass through the centre of the circle.

The perpendicular from the centre of a circle to a chord bisects the chord. The reason for this is as follows:

> **OX = OZ** (both radii)
> **OY = OY** (same line)
> **angle XYO = angle ZYO (90°)**

Therefore, the triangles **XOY** and **ZOY** are congruent (RHS, see page 60), which means that **XY = ZY.**

Circles

Circles and Angles

The following two pages have five more facts relating to circles and angles. You need to know them and their proofs.

Circles and Angles	Proofs
1 **Angles subtended by an arc** The angle at the centre of a circle, subtended by an arc, is **twice** the angle subtended at any point on the circumference by the same arc. (**N.B.** The word subtended simply means to be produced by drawing straight lines.) Angle AOB = 2 × Angle ACB Reflex Angle AOB = 2 × Angle ADB	Triangle ACO is isosceles (OC and OA are equal) Angle OCA = x (angles in an isosceles triangle) Angle AOD = $2x$ (exterior angle of triangle AOC) Similarly, angle BOD = $2y$ 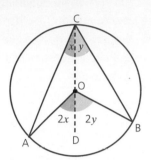 Angle AOB = $2x + 2y = 2(x + y)$ = **2 × Angle ACB**
2 **Angles subtended in the same segment** Angles subtended in the same segment are all equal. Here the angles subtended by the chord AB in the major segment are equal. The angles subtended by the chord AB in the minor segment are also equal. 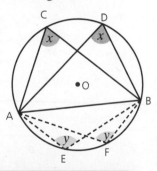 Angle ACB = Angle ADB Angle AEB = Angle AFB	$A\hat{O}B = 2 \times A\hat{C}B$ (angles subtended by an arc – see **1**) $A\hat{O}B = 2 \times A\hat{D}B$ (angles subtended by an arc – see **1**) ∴ $A\hat{C}B = A\hat{D}B$ 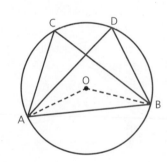
3 **Angles subtended by a semicircle** The angles subtended by a semicircle are always 90°. Angle ACB = Angle ADB = 90°	Let angle CAO = x and so angle ACO = x (isosceles triangle). Angle BOC = $2x$ (exterior angle of triangle AOC) ∴ $B\hat{C}O = \dfrac{180° - B\hat{O}C}{2} = \dfrac{180° - 2x}{2} = 90° - x$ (isosceles triangle) $A\hat{C}B = A\hat{C}O + B\hat{C}O = x + (90° - x) = \mathbf{90°}$

Circles

Circles and Angles	Proofs

④ Opposite angles of a cyclic quadrilateral

Opposite angles of a cyclic quadrilateral add up to 180°. A cyclic quadrilateral is a quadrilateral whose vertices (corners) all lie on the circumference of the same circle.

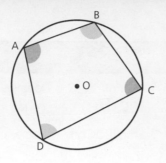

> Angle BAD + Angle BCD = 180°

> Angle ABC + Angle ADC = 180°

Let $B\hat{O}D = 2x$

$\therefore B\hat{A}D = \dfrac{B\hat{O}D}{2} = \dfrac{2x}{2} = x$

(angles subtended by an arc)

Reflex $B\hat{O}D = 360° - 2x$
(angles at a point)

$\therefore BCD = \dfrac{\text{Reflex } B\hat{O}D}{2} = \dfrac{360° - 2x}{2}$

$= 180° - x$ (angles subtended by an arc)

$B\hat{A}D + B\hat{C}D = x + (180° - x) = 180°$

Consequently $\mathbf{A\hat{B}C + A\hat{D}C = 180°}$
(angles of a quadrilateral = 360°)

⑤ Alternate segment theorem

The angle subtended between a tangent to a circle and its chord is equal to the angle subtended in the alternate segment.

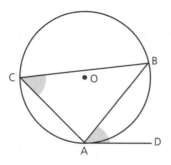

> Angle ACB = Angle BAD

Let angle BAD = x and triangle ABE have AE as diameter.

Angle ABE = 90° (angle subtended by a semicircle)

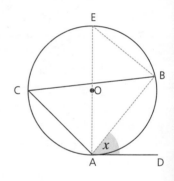

Angle BAE = 90° - x (angle between tangent and radius = 90°).

Angle BAE + Angle ABE = 90° - x + 90° = 180° - x
Angle AEB = x (angles in a triangle)
Angle ACB = angle AEB
(angles subtended in the same segment)
Angle ACB = angle BAD.

Example

Calculate angle ABC

> One method is to apply the alternate segment theorem twice

Angle ABD = 47°
Angle DBC = 32°
Angle ABC = 47° + 32° = 79°.
As a check, angle ADC + 47° + 32° = 180° since the angles lie on a straight line.
Angle ADC = 101°.
Angle ABC + angle ADC = 180° (cyclic quadrilateral).
Angle ABC = 180° - 107° = 79°

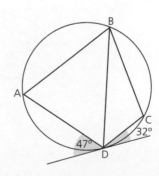

Net, Plans and Elevations

Plans and Elevations

This is a illustration of a car (a three-dimensional view of a solid).

It is possible for us to have three different views of the car:
- Plan view where we look down on the car from above.
- Front elevation where we look at the car from the front.
- Side elevation where we look at the car from the side.

Plan view   Front elevation   Side elevation

Examples

1️⃣

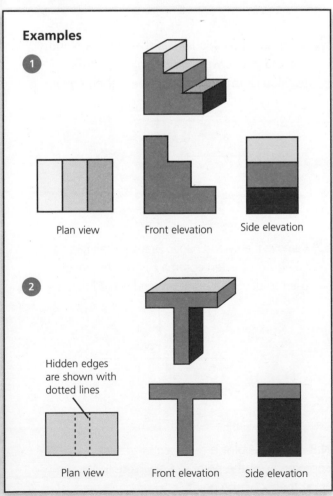

Plan view   Front elevation   Side elevation

2️⃣

Hidden edges are shown with dotted lines

Plan view   Front elevation   Side elevation

Nets for Solids

A **net** is a two-dimensional shape that can be folded to completely cover the outside of a solid.

Examples

1️⃣ Cube

2️⃣ Triangular prism

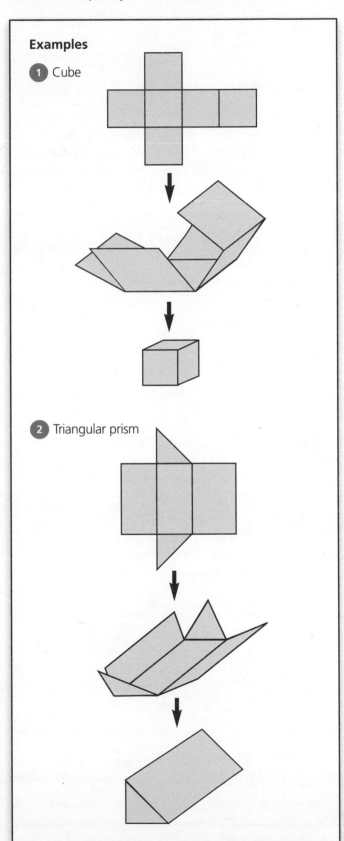

Transformations

Types of Transformations

A **transformation** acts on every point of a shape and may change its size, position and orientation. You need to know about the following types of transformation:

- **reflection**
- **rotation**
- **translation**
- **enlargement.**

If a point A is transformed, then the new point is usually labelled A'. The original point A is called the **object** and A' is called the **image**. Similarly, when a transformation is applied to a shape, the original shape is the object and the transformed shape is the image.

Reflection

A **mirror line** is needed to define a reflection. The image of every point lies on the opposite side of the mirror line to the object and is the same distance from the mirror line. A line drawn from the object to the image will cross the mirror line at right-angles.

To reflect a triangle ABC in a mirror line, find the image of each vertex and join them up to make triangle A'B'C'.

Examples

A mirror line is often described by giving its equation. The mirror lines $x = 6$ and $y = 1$ are used in the diagrams above.

When a shape is reflected the image is **congruent** to the object, which means corresponding lengths and angles are unchanged (see page 60).

Tracing paper may be used to reflect a shape. This is particularly useful when the mirror line is slanted, like in the example below.

To reflect triangle ABC in the line $y = x$…

1 Mark two points (• and •) on your mirror line.

2 On the tracing paper, draw in the mirror line, mark points and object carefully on the tracing paper, and then flip the tracing paper over (don't just rotate it).

3 Make sure that you line up the mirror line and marked points with the original. Mark the position of **image** through the tracing paper.

4 Remove the tracing paper. Draw in the image and label. An inverted comma (') after the label is used to denote a point on a reflected image.

N.B. When a point is reflected in the line $y = x$, the coordinates of the point are reversed. If A is the point (x, y) then A' is the point (y, x).

Transformations

Rotation

A rotation turns a shape through a clockwise or anti-clockwise angle about a fixed point known as the centre of rotation. All lines in the shape rotate through the same angle. Rotation, (just like reflection) changes the **orientation** and **position** of the shape, but everything else stays the same, i.e. lengths and angles. The object and image are congruent shapes (see page 60). To describe a rotation, you must specify the following three things:

- The direction of turn (clockwise / anti-clockwise)
- The centre of rotation
- The angle turned

Examples

1 Rotation of 90° clockwise about the origin (0,0)

2 Rotation of 180° about the origin (0,0)

> When the rotation is 180°, the direction of rotation is not needed

3 Rotation of 270° clockwise about the origin (0,0) (this is the same as a rotation of 90° anti-clockwise)

Difficult rotations can be completed more easily if you use tracing paper. For example, If we wanted to rotate triangle ABC 90° clockwise about the centre (-1,1)...

1 On the tracing paper, draw in axes and object.

2 Place point of compass on the centre of rotation (-1,1) and rotate paper clockwise.

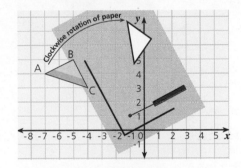

3 After 90° rotation, mark in position of image.

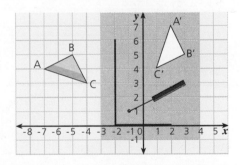

4 Remove the tracing paper. Draw in image and label.

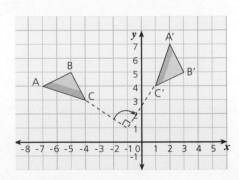

Transformations

Translation

A translation alters the position of a shape by moving every point of it by the same distance in the same direction. To describe a translation, you must specify the following two things:

- The direction of the movement
- The distance moved

This can be summarised using a **translation vector**, in which the movement in the x direction is placed directly above the movement in the y direction and both figures are surrounded by brackets. Positive and negative numbers are used to indicate the direction of the movement.

Examples

ABC has been translated to A''B''C'' by moving 11 squares to the left and then 4 squares down. This translation is written as a vector $\begin{pmatrix} -11 \\ -4 \end{pmatrix}$

ABC has been translated to A'B'C' by moving 7 squares to the right and then 2 squares up. This translation is written as a vector $\begin{pmatrix} 7 \\ 2 \end{pmatrix}$

ABC has been translated to A'''B'''C''' by moving 6 squares to the right and then 7 squares down. This translation is written as a vector $\begin{pmatrix} 6 \\ -7 \end{pmatrix}$

- Movement to the right (→) or up (▲) is positive.
- Movement to the left (←) or down (▼) is negative.

Translation only changes the position of the shape. Everything else stays the same, i.e. lengths and angles. The object and image are congruent shapes (see page 60).

Difficult translations can be completed more easily if you use tracing paper. Notice that all points (P', Q', R', S', T' and U') in the following example have moved 6 squares to the right and 7 squares down.

1 This shape must be translated using the translation vector $\begin{pmatrix} 6 \\ -7 \end{pmatrix}$.

2 Trace the shape onto tracing paper.

3 Place the tracing paper in the correct position using any point, e.g. Q.

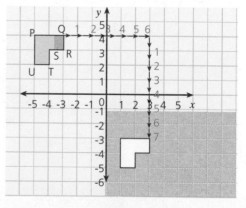

4 Draw over the image, first checking that it is correct.

Transformations

Enlargement

An enlargement changes the size of a shape. The shape can be made bigger or smaller according to the **scale factor**. All enlargements take place from one point called the **centre of enlargement**.

To describe an enlargement you must specify the following two things:
- The centre of enlargement
- The scale factor

Positive Scale Factor

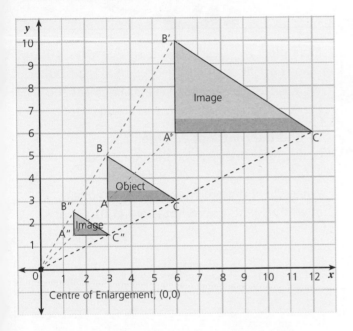

Centre of Enlargement, (0,0)

A scale factor greater than 1 means that the size of the image is bigger than the size of the object. Triangle A'B'C' is an enlargement of triangle ABC by a scale factor of 2, centre (0,0).

A'B' = 2 x AB		OA' = 2 x OA
A'C' = 2 x AC	and	OB' = 2 x OB
B'C' = 2 x BC		OC' = 2 x OC

A scale factor less than 1 means that the size of the image is smaller than the size of the object. Triangle A''B''C'' is an 'enlargement' of triangle ABC by a scale factor of $\frac{1}{2}$, centre (0,0).

A''B'' = $\frac{1}{2}$ x AB		OA'' = $\frac{1}{2}$ x OA
A''C'' = $\frac{1}{2}$ x AC	and	OB'' = $\frac{1}{2}$ x OB
B''C'' = $\frac{1}{2}$ x BC		OC'' = $\frac{1}{2}$ x OC

Enlargement only changes the size of the shape (i.e. the lengths of its sides) and its position.

Corresponding angles in the object and the image are the same, i.e. the shapes are **similar**. The orientation of the image is also the same as the object.

Sometimes you are asked to calculate the scale factor and find the centre of enlargement.

Example

Triangle P'Q'R' is an enlargement of triangle PQR. What is the scale factor of the enlargement and the coordinates of the centre of enlargement?

- **To find the centre of enlargement:**
  Draw dotted lines passing through P and P' (_____), Q and Q' (_____), R and R' (_____). Where these dotted lines cross is the centre of enlargement. **Coordinates are (0, 1)**.
- **To find the scale factor of the enlargement:**
  P'Q' = 10 units
  PQ = 2 units
  ∴ P'Q' = 5 × PQ

  Scale factor of the enlargement is 5.

N.B. The scale factor of an enlargement is a length scale factor. The scale factor for the area is different.

Area of triangle PQR = 1 square unit
Area of triangle P'Q'R' = 25 square units
Area scale factor = $25 = 5^2$

In general, if the scale factor of an enlargement is k then the area scale factor is k^2.

Transformations

Enlargement with a Negative Scale Factor

With a negative scale factor the number part of it tells us if the shape is to be made bigger or smaller, while the negative sign tells us that the image and object are on opposite sides of the centre of enlargement.

Triangle A'B'C' is an enlargement of triangle ABC by a scale factor of -2, centre (0,0).

A'B' = 2 × AB		OA' = 2 × OA
A'C' = 2 × AC	and	OB' = 2 × OB
B'C' = 2 × BC		OC' = 2 × OC

Triangle A"B"C" is an 'enlargement' of triangle ABC by a scale factor of $-\frac{1}{2}$, centre (0,0).

A"B" = $\frac{1}{2}$ × AB		OA" = $\frac{1}{2}$ × OA
A"C" = $\frac{1}{2}$ × AC	and	OB" = $\frac{1}{2}$ × OB
B"C" = $\frac{1}{2}$ × BC		OC" = $\frac{1}{2}$ × OC

Example

Triangle P'Q'R' is an enlargement of triangle PQR. What is the scale factor of the enlargement and the coordinates of the centre of enlargement?

To find the centre of enlargement:
Draw dotted lines passing through P and P' (_____), Q and Q' (_____), R and R' (_____). Where these dotted lines cross is the centre of enlargement. **Coordinates are (1,0)**

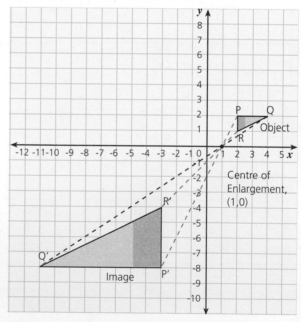

To find the scale factor of the enlargement:
P'Q' = 8 units, PQ = 2 units ∴ P'Q' = 4 × PQ.

Scale factor of the enlargement is -4.

N.B. Remember it is **negative** because the image and the object are on opposite sides of the centre of enlargement.

Transformations

Combination of Transformations

Very often a combination of two (or more) transformations can be described by a single transformation.

Examples

1 Triangle ABC is reflected in the *y*-axis to A'B'C' and then A'B'C' is reflected in the *x*-axis to A''B''C''.

Draw the two transformations and describe fully the single transformation that maps triangle ABC onto triangle A''B''C''.

Reflection in the *y*-axis

Reflection in the *x*-axis

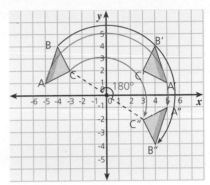

The single transformation is a rotation of 180° about the origin

2 Shape A is rotated 90° clockwise about the origin to shape B. Shape B is then reflected in the *x*-axis to shape C.

Draw the two transformations and describe fully the single transformation that maps shape A onto shape C.

Rotation of 90° clockwise about the origin

Reflection in the *x*-axis

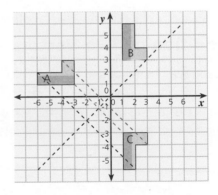

The single transformation is a reflection in the line *y* = *x*

A Summary of the Characteristics of Transformations

Transformation	You need to specify...	Properties that are preserved	Properties that change	Congruent or Similar?
Reflection	• The mirror line (equation of the line of reflection)	Shape and size (e.g. angles, lengths of sides)	Orientation, position	Congruent
Rotation	• Direction of turn • Centre of rotation • Angle turned through	Shape and size (e.g. angles, lengths of sides)	Orientation, position	Congruent
Translation	• Direction of movement • Distance moved	Shape and size (e.g. angles, lengths of sides) and orientation	Position	Congruent
Enlargement	• Centre of enlargement • Scale factor	Angles, ratios of lengths of side, orientation	Position, size	Similar

Vectors

Vectors

Vectors are quantities that have both **magnitude** (or size) and **direction**.

A common example of a vector quantity is displacement, which is distance moved in a particular direction. Another example is velocity, which is speed in a particular direction.

A vector is usually drawn as a **line with an arrow on it** where the length of the line represents magnitude (size) and the arrow represents direction. A and B are two points as shown below.

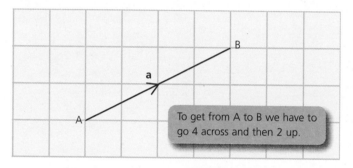

> To get from A to B we have to go 4 across and then 2 up.

The displacement of A to B can be described in the following way:

$\overrightarrow{AB} = \mathbf{a} = \begin{pmatrix} 4 \\ 2 \end{pmatrix}$. This is called a **column vector**.

Addition of Two Vectors

To add two vectors **a** and **b** graphically all we do is draw the second vector **b** so that it starts at the end of the first vector **a**. The resultant vector **a + b** is given by the vector which completes the triangle set up by **a** and **b**.

A* Tip

When using vectors, check that they go end to end so that the arrows follow on and do not oppose each other. Always try to simplify your answer.

Also, $\mathbf{a} = \begin{pmatrix} 4 \\ 1 \end{pmatrix}$ and $\mathbf{b} = \begin{pmatrix} 2 \\ 4 \end{pmatrix}$ which gives us:

$\mathbf{a} + \mathbf{b} = \begin{pmatrix} 4 \\ 1 \end{pmatrix} + \begin{pmatrix} 2 \\ 4 \end{pmatrix} = \begin{pmatrix} 4+2 \\ 1+4 \end{pmatrix} = \begin{pmatrix} 6 \\ 5 \end{pmatrix}$

The resultant of the addition of vectors **a** and **b** can also be thought of as the vector **a + b** along the diagonal SQ of the parallelogram PQRS as shown in this diagram.

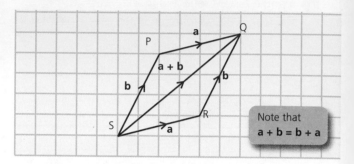

> Note that
> **a + b = b + a**

Subtraction of Two Vectors

To subtract two vectors **a** and **b** graphically, you first reverse the direction of the second vector so that **b** now becomes **-b**. Draw **-b** so that it starts at the end of **a**. The resultant vector **a – b** is again given by the vector that completes the triangle set up by **a** and **-b**.

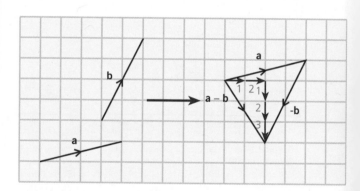

Also, $\mathbf{a} = \begin{pmatrix} 4 \\ 1 \end{pmatrix}$ and $\mathbf{b} = \begin{pmatrix} 2 \\ 4 \end{pmatrix}$ which gives us:

$\mathbf{a} - \mathbf{b} = \begin{pmatrix} 4 \\ 1 \end{pmatrix} - \begin{pmatrix} 2 \\ 4 \end{pmatrix} = \begin{pmatrix} 4-2 \\ 1-4 \end{pmatrix} = \begin{pmatrix} 2 \\ -3 \end{pmatrix}$

The result of the subtraction of vectors **a** and **b** can also be thought of as the vector **a – b** along the diagonal SQ of the parallelogram PQRS as shown in this diagram.

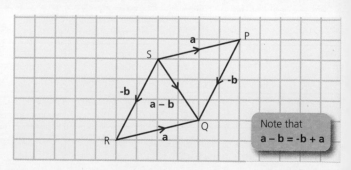

> Note that
> **a – b = -b + a**

Vector Proofs and 3-D Coordinates

Vectors may be used to prove some results in geometry.
This is something that may be required in an exam question.

Examples

1 In triangle ABC, G is the midpoint of AB and H is the midpoint of AC. If $\overrightarrow{AG}$ = **a** and $\overrightarrow{AH}$ = **b**:
a) Find expressions for $\overrightarrow{BC}$ and $\overrightarrow{GH}$ in terms of **a** and **b**.
b) Using your answers to part a) what two properties can you prove about BC and GH?

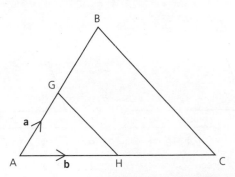

a) $\overrightarrow{BC}$ = $\overrightarrow{BA}$ + $\overrightarrow{AC}$
   = -2**a** + 2**b**

> To get from B to C we have to go from B to A ($\overrightarrow{BA}$) and then from A to C ($\overrightarrow{AC}$).
> $\overrightarrow{BA}$ = -$\overrightarrow{AB}$ = -2**a**

$\overrightarrow{GH}$ = $\overrightarrow{GA}$ + $\overrightarrow{AH}$
   = -**a** + **b**

b) Since…
$\overrightarrow{GH}$ = -**a** + **b**
and…
$\overrightarrow{BC}$ = -2**a** + 2**b**
   = 2(-**a** + **b**)
   = 2$\overrightarrow{GH}$

this proves that…
i) BC has twice the length of GH
ii) BC and GH are parallel.

2 P, Q, R and S are the midpoints of sides AB, BC, CD and DA of quadrilateral ABCD respectively. If $\overrightarrow{AB}$ = **a**, $\overrightarrow{AC}$ = **b** and $\overrightarrow{AD}$ = **c**, prove that PQRS is a parallelogram.

PQRS is a parallelogram providing that we can prove that PQ and SR are equal in length and parallel.

Firstly, let us determine $\overrightarrow{BC}$ and $\overrightarrow{DC}$ in terms of **a**, **b** and **c**.

$\overrightarrow{BC}$ = $\overrightarrow{BA}$ + $\overrightarrow{AC}$ and $\overrightarrow{DC}$ = $\overrightarrow{DA}$ + $\overrightarrow{AC}$
   = -**a** + **b**   = -**c** + **b**

We will now prove that $\overrightarrow{PQ}$ = $\overrightarrow{SR}$:
$\overrightarrow{PQ}$ = $\overrightarrow{PB}$ + $\overrightarrow{BQ}$
   = $\frac{1}{2}\overrightarrow{AB}$ + $\frac{1}{2}\overrightarrow{BC}$
   = $\frac{1}{2}$**a** + $\frac{1}{2}$(-**a** + **b**)
   = $\frac{1}{2}$**a** $-\frac{1}{2}$**a** + $\frac{1}{2}$**b** = $\frac{1}{2}$**b**
$\overrightarrow{SR}$ = $\overrightarrow{SD}$ + $\overrightarrow{DR}$
   = $\frac{1}{2}\overrightarrow{AD}$ + $\frac{1}{2}\overrightarrow{DC}$
   = $\frac{1}{2}$**c** + $\frac{1}{2}$(-**c** + **b**)
   = $\frac{1}{2}$**c** $-\frac{1}{2}$**c** + $\frac{1}{2}$**b** = $\frac{1}{2}$**b**

$\overrightarrow{PQ}$ = $\overrightarrow{SR}$, which means that PQ and SR are equal in length and are parallel; PQRS is therefore a parallelogram.

3-D Coordinates

Three coordinates are needed to identify a point in space, i.e. in 3-D (in three dimensions). Three axes each at right angles to each other are needed. The coordinates of each point represent distances from 0, a fixed point, firstly parallel to the x-axis then parallel to the y-axis, and finally parallel to the z-axis.

Example

> Point A is (4,3,2) since we need to go 4 units parallel to the x-axis, then 3 units parallel to the y-axis and finally 2 units parallel to the z-axis.

Constructions

Construction of Triangles

In your exams, you must show all construction lines.

3 sides given: Construct the triangle ABC where AB = 3cm, BC = 2.5cm and AC = 2cm

Draw AB of length 3cm

Draw arc from A of radius 2cm

Draw arc from B of radius 2.5cm

Complete the triangle

2 sides and the included angle given: Construct the triangle ABC where AB = 3cm, AC = 2cm and $B\hat{A}C$ = 70°

Draw AB of length 3cm

At A, measure and mark angle of 70°

Draw AC of length 2cm

Complete the triangle

2 sides and the non-included angle given: Construct the triangle ABC where AB = 2cm, AC = 2cm and $A\hat{B}C$ = 50°

Draw AB of length 2cm

At B, measure, mark and draw angle of 50°

Draw arc from A of radius 2cm

Complete the triangle

1 side and 2 angles given: Construct the triangle ABC where AB = 3cm, $B\hat{A}C$ = 50° and $A\hat{B}C$ = 30°

Draw AB of length 3cm

At A, measure, mark and draw angle of 50°

At B, measure and mark angle of 30°

Complete the triangle

Construction of an Angle of 60° and 90°

Angle of 60°

Draw arc from A to cross AB at P

Draw another arc from A of same radius

Draw arc from P (again same radius)

Complete the angle

Angle of 90°

Extend A with a dotted line to C. Draw two arcs from A (same radius) to cross CB at P and Q

Draw arc from P of longer radius than in previous diagram

Draw arc from Q (same radius as previous diagram)

Complete the angle

Constructions

The Midpoint and Perpendicular Bisector of a Line Segment

Draw arcs of equal radius from points A and B to intersect at C.

Draw arcs of the same radius on the other side of the line to intersect at D.

Join C to D to form the perpendicular bisector, (or to locate the midpoint).

The Perpendicular from a Point to a Line

Draw two arcs from 0 to cross AB at P and Q.

Draw arc from P.

Draw arc from Q (using same radius as previous diagram).

Complete the perpendicular.

The Perpendicular from a Point on a Line

Draw arcs of equal radius from point 0, to cross AB at P and Q.

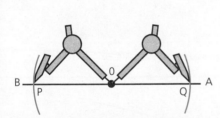

Draw arcs of the same radius (but greater than step 1) from P and Q to intersect at R.

Join 0 to R to form the perpendicular from point 0.

The Bisector of an Angle

This construction may be combined with the construction of angles 60° and 90° to give angles of 30° and 45°.

Draw arcs of equal radius from point A to cut lines at B and C.

Draw arcs of equal radius from points B and C to intersect at point D.

Join A to D to form the bisector of the angle.

Loci

Locus

A locus is a set of points that satisfy some condition. Depending on the condition, the set of points may lie on a line or cover an area inside a shape.

The locus of points that are always at a constant distance from a point is a circle whose radius is equal to the constant distance.

The locus of points that are always at a constant distance from a line is a pair of parallel lines, one above and one below the line with a pair of semi-circles, one at each end of the line.

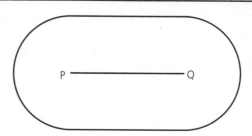

The locus of points that are always equidistant from two points is a line that bisects the line between the two points at right angles (i.e. a perpendicular bisector).

The locus of points that are further from P than Q lie in the region to the right of the perpendicular bisector. In this case, the line itself would be shown dotted to show that it is not included.

The locus of points that are always equidistant from two diverging lines is a line that bisects the angle between the two lines (i.e. an angle bisector).

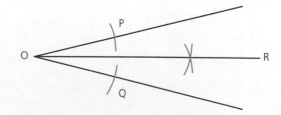

The locus of points closer to OP than OQ lie above OR. Again, the line itself would be shown dotted to show that it is not included.

Perimeter and Circumference

Perimeter

Perimeter is the distance all the way around the outside of a shape. It is measured in units of length such as cm or m.

Example

The lengths of all the sides are given or can be worked out and so...

Perimeter = AB + BC + CD + DE + EF + FA
= 6 + 2.5 + 4 + (4.1 − 2.5) + 2 + 4.1
= **20.2cm**

OR BC + DE = 4.1cm
Perimeter = 2 × 6cm + 2 × 4.1cm
= 12cm + 8.2cm
= **20.2cm**

Circumference of a Circle

Circumference is the mathematical word for the perimeter of a circle. The **radius** is the distance from the centre, ● , to the outside of the circle. The **diameter** is the distance from one side of the circle through the centre, ● , to the other side of the circle.

Radius = $\frac{1}{2}$ × diameter   i.e. $r = \frac{1}{2}d$

or Diameter = 2 × radius   i.e. $d = 2r$

The circumference of a circle is given by:

Circumference = π × diameter   i.e. $C = \pi d$
or **Circumference = 2 × π × radius   i.e. $C = 2\pi r$**

Examples

1 Calculate the circumference of this circle (to 3 s.f.)

$r = 7.6$m
$C = 2\pi r$
= 2 × π × 7.6m
= 47.752... m
= **47.8m**

Alternatively, use $C = \pi d$ with $d = 2 \times 7.6 = 15.2$cm

2 This shape is made from semi-circles. Calculate the distance from A to B along the curve (to 3 s.f.).

$d = \frac{18\text{cm}}{3} = 6$cm

$C = \pi d = \pi \times 6$cm

A to B = 1.5C
= 1.5 × π × 6cm
= 28.274... cm
= **28.3cm**

3 Find an exact expression in terms of π for the perimeter of the diagram below.

Perimeter
= circumference of circle + lengths of straight sides
= (π × 18m) + (2 × 25m)
= **(18π + 50)m**

Arcs and Circumference

Length of an Arc

An arc is simply part of the circumference of a circle (see page 66).

The length of an arc is given by:

$$\text{Length of Arc} = \frac{\theta}{360°} \times 2\pi r$$

where θ is the angle at the centre of the circle

Major arc · Minor arc

---

1 Calculate the length of the minor arc **AB** in the following diagram (to 3 s.f.) For this question use $\pi \approx 3.14$

Length of minor arc
$$= \frac{50°}{360°} \times 2\pi r$$

$$= \frac{50}{360} \times 2 \times \pi \times 5\text{cm}$$

$$= 4.361\ldots \text{ cm}$$

$$= \mathbf{4.36cm}$$

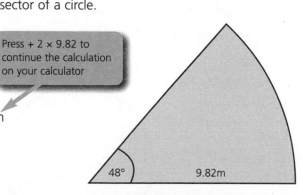

5cm A

0 50°

B

---

2 The diagram shows a garden flower bed in the shape of a sector of a circle. Calculate its perimeter (to 2 d.p.).

Length of arc
$$= \frac{48°}{360°} \times 2 \times \pi \times 9.82\text{m}$$

$$= \frac{48}{360} \times 2 \times \pi \times 9.82\text{m}$$

$$= 8.227\text{m (to 4 s.f.)}$$

Press + 2 × 9.82 to continue the calculation on your calculator

Perimeter
= length of arc + 2 × 9.82m
= 8.226… + 2 × 9.82m
= 27.866… m
= **27.87m**

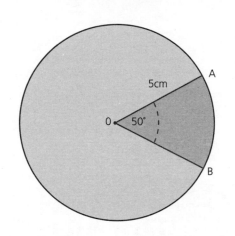

48° 9.82m

---

3 Find an exact expression for the perimeter of this shape in terms of π.

$r = 4$cm and the angle of the sector is 270°.

Length of arc
$$= \frac{270°}{360°} \times 2 \times \pi \times 4\text{cm}$$

$$= \frac{3}{4} \times 2 \times \pi \times 4\text{cm}$$

$$= 6\pi\text{cm}$$

Perimeter
= length of arc + 8cm
= **$(6\pi + 8)$cm**

4cm

Area

Area is a measure of the amount of surface covered by a shape. Area is measured in square units, e.g. cm² (cm squared), or m² (m squared).

To find the area of a square, rectangle or parallelogram, use the following formula:

Area = Base × Height

To find the area of a trapezium, use the following formula:

Area = $\frac{1}{2}(a + b)\,h$

or... $= \frac{(a + b)}{2} \times h$

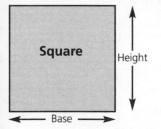

Square — Height — Base

Rectangle — Height — Base

Parallelogram — Height — Base

Trapezium — Height (h) — b — a

Examples

1. Calculate the area of the following trapezium.

Using our formula: Area $= \frac{(a + b)}{2} \times h$

Area $= \frac{(10m + 6m)}{2} \times 4m$

$= \frac{16m}{2} \times 4m$

$= 8m \times 4m$

$= 32m^2$

2. The following parallelogram has an area of 24cm². Calculate its height if the length of its base is 10cm.

Using our formula: Area = Base × Height

$24cm^2 = 10cm \times Height$

$\frac{24}{10} = \frac{\cancel{10}}{\cancel{10}} \times Height$

> Divide both sides by 10 to give the height on its own

Height = 2.4cm

3. The diagram shows part of a kitchen wall that is to be tiled.

The tiles are 10cm square and are sold in boxes of 20. Each box costs £18.

a) Calculate the total cost of the tiles needed.

b) Calculate the cost per m² of using the tiles (to 2 d.p.).

a) The middle section of the wall has length
200cm − 60cm − 60cm = 80cm

Number of tiles needed = (6×3)+(8×2)+(6×3)
= 52

Number of boxes needed = 3
Total cost = 3 × £18 = **£54**

b) Area covered = (2m × 0.3m) − (0.8m × 0.1m)
= 0.52m²

Cost per m² = £54 ÷ 0.52 = £103.846...
= £103.85 to the nearest penny

Area of Triangles and Circles

Area of a Triangle

The area of a triangle can be found very simply (if we know the length of its base and height) using the following formula:

$$\text{Area} = \frac{1}{2} \times \text{base} \times \text{height}$$
$$\text{or...} = \frac{\text{base} \times \text{height}}{2}$$

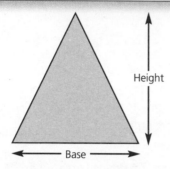

However, we can also work out its area if we know the length of two of the sides and their included angle. The formula is:

$$\text{Area} = \frac{1}{2}\,ab\sin C$$

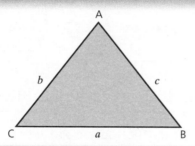

Example
Calculate the area of the following triangle (to 3 s.f.).

$$\text{Area} = \frac{1}{2}\,ab\sin C$$
$$= \frac{1}{2} \times 8 \times 6.4 \times \sin 35° \text{ cm}^2$$
$$= 14.68... \text{ cm}^2$$
$$= \textbf{14.7cm}^2$$

Area of a Circle

The area of a circle is given by the following formula:

$$\textbf{Area} = \pi r^2$$

Examples

1 Calculate the area of a circle of radius 8.6cm (to 3 s.f.).

$$\text{Area} = \pi r^2$$
$$= \pi \times 8.6^2$$
$$= 232.35... \text{ cm}^2$$
$$= \textbf{232cm}^2$$

2 Calculate the shaded area in the diagram (to 3 s.f.).

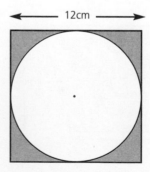

Area of square $= 12^2 = 144\text{cm}^2$

Area of circle $= \pi \times 6^2$
$$= 113.097... \text{ cm}^2$$

Shaded area $= 144 - 113.097... \text{ cm}^2$
$$= \textbf{30.9cm}^2$$

Surface Area and Sectors

Area of a Sector

A sector is the area enclosed by two radii and an arc. It can be major or minor (see page 66).

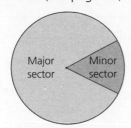

The area of a sector is given by the following formula:

> **Area of Sector** $= \dfrac{\theta}{360°} \times \pi r^2$
>
> where θ is the angle at the centre of the circle.

Example

Calculate the area of the minor sector in the following diagram (to 3 s.f.).

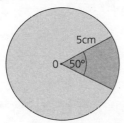

$$
\begin{aligned}
\text{Area of minor sector} &= \frac{\theta}{360°} \times \pi r^2 \\
&= \frac{50°}{360°} \times \pi \times 5^2 \\
&= \frac{50}{360} \times \pi \times 25 \\
&= 10.90\ldots \text{ cm}^2 \\
&= \mathbf{10.9 cm^2}
\end{aligned}
$$

Area of a Segment

Example

Find the area of the shaded segment (to 1 d.p.).

Area of sector $= \dfrac{80}{360} \times \pi \times 5^2$

area of triangle $= \dfrac{1}{2}\,ab \sin C = \dfrac{1}{2} \times 5 \times 5 \times \sin 80°$

$\therefore$ area of segment $= \dfrac{80}{360} \times \pi \times 5^2 - \dfrac{1}{2} \times 5 \times 5 \times \sin 80°$

$$= \mathbf{5.1 cm^2}$$

Surface Area of Solids

The surface area of any solid is simply the area of the **net** which can be folded to completely cover the outside of the solid (see page 69).

Examples

1 Calculate the surface area of the following triangular prism, which has an equilateral triangle as its cross-section.

Area of 1 (Rectangle) = 10cm × 4cm = 40cm²
Therefore, area of 1 + 2 + 3 = 120cm²

Area of 4 (Triangle) $= \dfrac{4cm \times 3.5cm}{2} = 7cm^2$
Therefore, area of 5 + 4 = 14cm²

$$
\text{Surface area of prism} = \text{Area of } 1 + 2 + 3 + 4 + 5
$$

$$= 120cm^2 + 14cm^2$$
$$= \mathbf{134 cm^2}$$

2 Calculate the surface area of this cylinder (to 1 d.p.) $\pi \approx 3.14$

Area of each end $= \pi r^2$
$$= 3.14 \times 1.5^2$$
$$= 7.065 cm^2$$

$\therefore$ both ends = 7.065 × 2 = 14.13cm²

Length of x = circumference of circle
$= 2\pi r = 2 \times 3.14 \times 1.5$
$= 9.42$cm

$\therefore$ area of rectangle = 7 × 9.42
= 65.94cm²

Therefore, total area
= 14.13cm² + 65.94cm² = 80.07cm²
= **80.1cm²**

Volume

Volume

Volume is a measure of the amount of space a 3-D object takes up. It is usually measured in **units³**, e.g. **cm³** (cm cubed) or **m³** (m cubed).

Calculation of the Volume of a Solid Made Up of Cubes

Providing we know the volume of one cube then all we have to do is work out how many cubes there are in each layer of the solid and then add them up.

Example

In the following example each cube has a volume of 1cm³.

This solid is made up of two layers

Bottom layer   Top layer

 +

Volume = 6 cubes + 3 cubes
$$= 6cm^3 + 3cm^3$$
$$= \textbf{9cm}^3$$

Volume of a Cuboid

Volume = Length × Width × Height
$$V = l \times w \times h$$

Example

Using our formula:
Volume = length × width × height
$$= 6cm \times 4cm \times 2cm$$
$$= \textbf{48cm}^3$$

Volume of a Prism

A prism is a solid that has a uniform cross-section from one end of the solid to the other end.

Volume of a prism = area of cross-section × length

Example

Calculate the volume of the triangular prism.

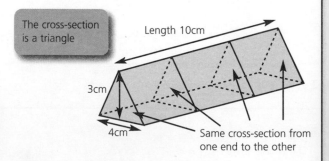

The cross-section is a triangle

Length 10cm

3cm

4cm

Same cross-section from one end to the other

Using our formula:
Volume = area of cross-section × length
$$= \frac{(base \times height)}{2} \times length$$
$$= \frac{(4cm \times 3cm)}{2} \times 10cm$$
$$= 6cm^2 \times 10cm$$
$$= \textbf{60cm}^3$$

Volume

Volume of a Cylinder

A cylinder is a prism that has a uniform cross-section of a circle from one end of the prism to the other. The volume of any cylinder is given by the formula:

Volume of a cylinder = $\pi r^2 l = \pi r^2 \times l$
(where l is the length of the cylinder)

Length

Cross-section is a circle

Examples

1. Calculate the volume of the following cylinder (to 3 s.f.).

8cm

2cm

Using our formula:
Volume $= \pi r^2 l$
$= \pi \times 2^2 \times 8 \text{cm}^3 = 100.5... \text{cm}^3$
= 101cm³

2. A cylindrical tank is 1.6m long and holds 0.8m³ of oil when full. What is the radius of the cylinder (to 1 s.f.)?

Using our formula:
Volume $= \pi r^2 l$
$0.8 = \pi \times r^2 \times 1.6$
$\dfrac{0.8}{\pi \times 1.6} = r^2$
$0.1591... = r^2$
$r = \sqrt{0.1591...}$
$r = 0.3989...$
radius = 0.4m

1.6m

Volume of a Pyramid

Volume $= \dfrac{1}{3} \times$ Area of Base $\times$ Vertical Height

Vertical height

Base

Vertical height

Base

Volume of a Sphere

Volume $= \dfrac{4}{3} \times \pi \times (\text{radius})^3$

$= \dfrac{4}{3}\pi r^3$

Example

Calculate the radius of a sphere of volume 500cm³ (to 3 s.f.)

$\dfrac{4}{3}\pi r^3 = 500$

$r^3 = \dfrac{3 \times 500}{4\pi}$

$r = \sqrt[3]{\left(\dfrac{3 \times 500}{4\pi}\right)} = \mathbf{4.92cm}$

Volume = 500cm³

Volume of a Cone

Volume $= \dfrac{1}{3} \times$ Area of Base $\times$ Vertical Height

$= \dfrac{1}{3}\pi r^2 h$

h

r

Example

Calculate the volume of the solid (to 1 d.p.).

5cm

3cm

B   C

5cm

A

D   6cm   E

$$\text{Volume of solid} = \text{Volume of cone ADE} - \text{Volume of cone ABC}$$

Volume of cone **ADE** $= \dfrac{1}{3} \times \pi \times 6^2 \times 10$
$= 376.99... \text{ cm}^3$

Volume of cone **ABC** $= \dfrac{1}{3} \times \pi \times 3^2 \times 5$
$= 47.12... \text{ cm}^3$

Volume of solid $= 376.99 \text{cm}^3 - 47.12 \text{cm}^3$
$= 329.87... \text{ cm}^3$
= 329.9cm³

Maps and Scale Drawings

Drawing to Size and Scale

Before you attempt to construct any drawing to a particular size or scale you need the following items:

- A **pencil** and **rubber** so any mistakes can be rubbed out.
- A **ruler** for drawing straight lines.
- A **protractor** for measuring angles.
- A **compass** for drawing circles, arcs and other constructions

Example

Here is a sketch map of an island. The map has four marker points A, B, C and D.

a) Make an accurate scale drawing of the quadrilateral ABCD using a scale of 1cm to represent 10km.

b) Calculate the length of BC.

a) Step 1: Draw the 90km line AD (9cm).
Step 2: Measure and mark 80° and 90°.
Step 3: Draw the 35km line (3.5cm) and the 45km line (4.5cm).
Step 4: Complete the quadrilateral.

b) Length of BC on diagram = 8.4cm.
Real distance of BC = 8.4 × 10km = **84km**

Map Scales

This is part of a map of Devon and Cornwall which is drawn to a scale of 1cm : 10km or 1 : 100000 (see page 20)

1 The direct distance from Newquay to Plymouth as measured on the map is 7cm. Calculate the actual distance.

Actual distance
= 7 × 10 = **70km**

2 The actual direct distance between Torquay and Exeter is 30km. Calculate the map distance.

Map distance
$= \frac{30}{10} = $ **3cm**

A scale of 1cm : 10km means that a distance of 1cm measured on the map is an actual distance of 10km.

Effects of Enlargement

Similar Figures

Similar figures are identical in their shape but they are not identical in their size (they can be bigger or smaller). The two figures (cuboids) below are similar.

Figure A

Figure B

From our two figures, the ratio of two corresponding lengths is $a : b$ (all other corresponding lengths will also be in the same ratio).

Area is a measure of 'length squared' (e.g. cm^2 or m^2) so the ratio of their areas is the ratio of the two corresponding lengths squared. To put it simply:

- **Ratio of their areas = $a^2 : b^2$**

Volume is a measure of 'length cubed' (e.g. cm^3 or m^3) so the ratio of their volumes is the ratio of the two corresponding lengths cubed. To put it simply:

- **Ratio of their volumes = $a^3 : b^3$**

Two important notes:

- If the ratio of the area of two similar figures is for example $9 : 16$ ($a^2 : b^2$) then the ratio of corresponding lengths will be $\sqrt{9} : \sqrt{16} = 3 : 4$. This means that to go from area to length you must square root the ratio for area.

  The ratio of their volumes will now be
  $3^3 : 4^3 = 27 : 64$ ($a^3 : b^3$)

- If the ratio of the volume of two similar figures is for example $8 : 125$ ($a^3 : b^3$) then the ratio of corresponding lengths will be $\sqrt[3]{8} : \sqrt[3]{125} = 2 : 5$. This means that to go from volume to length you must cube root the ratio for volume.

  The ratio of their areas will now be
  $2^2 : 5^2 = 4 : 25$ ($a^2 : b^2$)

A* Tip

When finding the area / volume of similar figures, first find the linear scale factor and use this to square or cube as appropriate. If you are given the area / volume scale factors you will need to use square or cube roots.

Examples

1 Figures A and B are similar. If the surface area of Figure A is $52cm^2$ and its volume is $24cm^3$ calculate…
a) the surface area of Figure B
b) the volume of Figure B.

Figure A

Figure B

We know that the ratio of two corresponding lengths, $a : b$, is $4 : 6$ which is the equal to $2 : 3$

a) Ratio of areas $= a^2 : b^2$
   $= 2^2 : 3^2$ *i.e. 4 parts to 9 parts*
   $= 4 : 9$

For Figure A: 4 parts $= 52cm^2$
1 part $= \dfrac{52}{4} = 13cm^2$

Figure B is equal to 9 parts
$= 9 \times 13cm^2$
$= 117cm^2$

∴ **Surface area of Figure B = $117cm^2$**

b) Ratio of volumes $= a^3 : b^3$
   $= 2^3 : 3^3$
   $= 8 : 27$

For Figure A: 8 parts $= 24cm^3$
1 part $= \dfrac{24}{8} = 3cm^3$

Figure B is equal to 27 parts
$= 27 \times 3cm^3$
$= 81cm^3$

∴ **Volume of Figure B = $81cm^3$**

2 The surface areas of two similar objects are $80cm^2$ and $180cm^2$. The volume of the smaller object is $64cm^3$. What is the volume of the larger object?

The surface areas are in the ratio $80 : 180 = 4 : 9$
Corresponding lengths must be in the ratio $2 : 3$
The volumes are in the ratio $8 : 27$
Volume of larger object $= \dfrac{64}{8} \times 27 =$ **$216cm^3$**

Converting Measurements

Metric and Imperial Units

	Metric Units		Approximate Comparison between Metric and Imperial		Imperial Units	
Length	10mm	= 1cm	2.5cm ≈ 1 inch		12 inches	= 1 foot
	100cm	= 1m	1m ≈ 39 inches		3 feet	= 1 yard
	1000m	= 1km	1600m ≈ 1 mile		1760 yards	= 1 mile
			8km ≈ 5 miles			
Mass	1000mg	= 1g	30g ≈ 1 ounce		16 ounces	= 1 pound
	1000g	= 1kg	450g ≈ 1 pound		14 pounds	= 1 stone
	1000kg	= 1 tonne	1kg ≈ 2.2 pounds			
Capacity or Volume	1000ml	= 1l	1l ≈ $1\frac{3}{4}$ pints		8 pints	= 1 gallon
	1000cm³	= 1l	4.5l ≈ 1 gallon			
	(1ml	= 1cm³)				

Converting One Metric Unit to Another

Consider the conversion between centimetres (cm) and metres (m) as a typical example:

Divide (÷) by 100 as we are going from a bigger number (100) to a smaller number (1)

100cm   100cm = 1m   1m

Multiply (×) by 100 as we are going from a smaller number (1) to a bigger number (100)

Examples

1 Penny is 1.65m tall. What is her height in centimetres?

From above: m $\xrightarrow{\times 100}$ cm

1.65m = 1.65 × 100 = **165cm**

2 Write 370mm² in cm².

10mm = 1cm (square both sides),
so 100mm² = 1cm²

$370mm^2 = \frac{370}{100} = \mathbf{3.7cm^2}$

Converting Between Metric and Imperial Units

Converting between metric and imperial follows the same rules as converting metric units. Take the conversion between grams (g) and pounds as an example.

Divide (÷) by 450

450g   450g ≈ 1 pound   1 pound

Multiply (×) by 450

Examples

1 A tin of baked beans has a mass of 600g. What is its mass in pounds?

From above: g $\xrightarrow{\div 450}$ pounds

$600g = \frac{600}{450} = \mathbf{1.33\ pounds}$ (approx.)

2 A recipe for a cake needs 1.5 pounds of flour. What mass of flour is needed in grams?

From above: pounds $\xrightarrow{\times 450}$ g

1.5 pounds = 1.5 × 450 = **675g** (approx.)

Bearings

Three-figure Bearings

A bearing is a measurement of the position of one point relative to another point. It is measured in degrees. **Bearings are always measured from the north in a clockwise direction and are given as three digits**. Below are two points, A and B. There are two possible bearings:

- The bearing of B from point A. This means that the measurement of the bearing is taken **from point A**.
- The bearing of A from point B. This means that the measurement of the bearing is taken **from point B**.

1 Draw in North (N) direction.

2 Measure angle from N direction in a clockwise direction.

3 Angle = 180° + 120° = 300°

4 Bearing of A from B is 300°

1 Draw in North (N) direction.

2 Measure angle from N direction in a clockwise direction.

3 Angle = 120°

4 Bearing of B from A is 120°

A circular protractor with a full 360° range can make three-figure bearings much easier to measure.

Sometimes the angle you measure from the N direction is less than 100° or even less than 10°. In this case one or two zeros are put in front of the angle in order to make them three-figure bearings.

Example

The bearing of B from A is **075°**. Find the bearing of A from B.

To find the bearing of A from B we need an extended North line at B.

Since the two North lines are parallel, it follows that $x = 75°$ (alternate angles).

Bearing of A from B = 180° + 75° = **255°**

A* Tip

Make sure you are competent at finding back-bearings from standard bearings.

Compound Measures

Speed

Speed is a measure of 'how fast' an object is moving. To calculate the speed of a moving object we need two measurements:

- The **distance** it moves.
- The **time** it takes to move that distance.

Speed is measured in metres per second (m/s), kilometres per hour (km/h) or miles per hour (mph).

Speed can be calculated using the following formula:

$$\text{Speed (S)} = \frac{\text{Distance (D)}}{\text{Time (T)}}$$

Strictly speaking, the formula gives the average speed over the given distance because its value may vary.

The formula $S = \dfrac{D}{T}$ may be rearranged to give $D = ST$ and $T = \dfrac{D}{S}$.

Each of these variations may be useful depending on what you need to calculate to solve a problem.

Mathematicians tend to remember one version of a formula and rearrange it as necessary.

Examples

1. Calculate the speed of a car that travels a distance of 90m in 10s.

   $$\text{Speed} = \frac{90m}{10s} = 9m/s$$

2. A train completes a journey of 150km at an average speed of 90km/h. How long did the journey take?

   $$\text{Time} = \frac{\text{Distance}}{\text{Speed}} = \frac{150km}{90km/h} = 1.\dot{6} \text{ hours}$$

   $1\frac{2}{3}$ hours = **1 hour 40 minutes**

A* Tip

When answering a question on time, remember you are working in hours, minutes and seconds, i.e. use 60ths not 100ths.

Density

Density is a measure of 'how heavy' an object is 'per unit volume'. To calculate the density of an object we need two measurements:

- Its **mass**.
- Its **volume**.

Density is measured in grams per centimetre cubed, (g/cm^3) or kilograms per metre cubed, (kg/m^3).

Density can be calculated using the following formula:

$$\text{Density (D)} = \frac{\text{Mass (M)}}{\text{Volume (V)}}$$

The formula $D = \dfrac{M}{V}$ may be rearranged to give $M = DV$ and $V = \dfrac{M}{D}$.

Examples

1. Calculate the density of an object that has a mass of 75g and a volume of 100cm³.

   $$\text{Density} = \frac{75g}{100cm^3} = \mathbf{0.75g/cm^3}$$

2. An object of density 4.73g/cm³ has mass 25kg. Calculate the volume of the object (to 3 s.f.)

   M = 25kg = 2500g

   D = 4.73g/cm³

   $$V = \frac{M}{D} = \frac{2500}{4.73} = 528.5...cm^3 = \mathbf{529cm^3}$$

A* Tip

Make sure that you include the correct units as part of your answer.

Probability

The Nature of Probability

Probability is a measure of the likelihood that an event will occur.

To gain a good understanding of probability you need to learn the vocabulary used to describe it. This section develops the basic vocabulary within the context of an example.

Equally Likely Outcomes

The 12 coloured counters shown below are put into a bag and one is selected at random.

Because the counters are all the same size and shape, each one has an **equal chance** of being selected. The selection of a particular counter is called an **outcome**. In this case, there are 12 **equally likely outcomes** and we say that a counter is to be selected at **random**.

For example, there are five red counters so five of the possible outcomes are associated with the **event** of selecting a red counter. In general, an event involves some set of outcomes and we talk about the probability of an event, written as P(event).

When all of the outcomes are equally likely, the probability of an event is given by:

$$P(event) = \frac{\text{Number of outcomes in the event}}{\text{The total number of outcomes}}$$

Using R to represent the selection of a red counter:
$$P(R) = \frac{5}{12}$$

In the same way, $P(B) = \frac{4}{12}$ and $P(Y) = \frac{3}{12}$

Using R' to represent the event of **not** selecting a red counter gives

$P(R') = \frac{7}{12}$ ← 7 counters are not red

Notice that $P(R') = 1 - P(R)$.

As a general result:

For an event A, we use A' to represent the event that does not occur $P(A') = 1 - P(A)$

Mutually Exclusive Events

Mutually exclusive events are events that have no outcomes in common, i.e. one event is not dependent on the other event. The events R (Red), B (Blue) and Y (Yellow) given opposite are mutually exclusive because every counter has only one colour.

$P(R \text{ or } Y) = \frac{8}{12}$ ← 8 counters are red or yellow

Notice that $P(R \text{ or } Y) = P(R) + P(Y)$

In general:

For mutually exclusive events A and B: **P(A or B) = P(A) + P(B)**

We also have $P(R \text{ or } B \text{ or } Y) = \frac{5}{12} + \frac{4}{12} + \frac{3}{12} = \frac{12}{12} = 1$

In general: **The sum of the probabilities of a complete set of mutually exclusive outcomes is always 1.**

If A and B are **not** mutually exclusive events then P(A or B) is **not** equal to P(A) + P(B).

Example
A fair dice is rolled.
Let E be the event of obtaining an even score (2, 4, 6).
Let S be the event of obtaining a square number (1, 4).

These are not mutually independent events, therefore, not mutually exclusive

$P(E) = \frac{3}{6}$ $P(S) = \frac{2}{6}$ ← E and S have 4 as a common outcome

$P(E \text{ or } S) = \frac{4}{6} \neq \frac{3}{6} + \frac{2}{6}$

Probability

Outcomes of Single Events

- Flipping a coin – there are only two outcomes: Heads or Tails
- Throwing a dice – there are only six outcomes: One, Two, Three, Four, Five or Six

In cases like these, all you have to do is make a simple list.

Outcomes of Two Successive Events

1 Flipping two fair coins, one after the other
In cases like these it is easier to use a **sample space diagram** to show the possible outcomes.

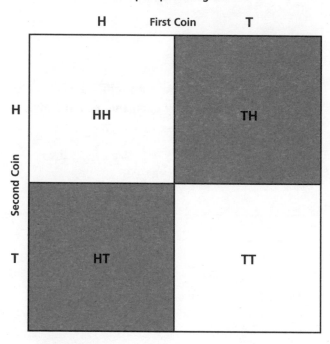

Sample Space Diagram

With two coins there are four outcomes. The chances of each outcome are…

P(Head + Head) $= \frac{1}{4}$

P(Tail + Tail) $= \frac{1}{4}$

P(Head + Tail) $= \frac{1}{4}$

P(Tail + Head) $= \frac{1}{4}$

N.B. Once again the probability of each outcome added together is 1, i.e. $\frac{1}{4} + \frac{1}{4} + \frac{1}{4} + \frac{1}{4} = 1$

2 Throwing a pair of fair dice
In this case, each dice has six possible outcomes. The sample space diagram, which shows the scores of the two dice added together, reveals a total of 36 possible outcomes.

Sample Space Diagram

	First Dice					
Second Dice	**1**	**2**	**3**	**4**	**5**	**6**
1	2	3	4	5	6	7
2	3	4	5	6	7	8
3	4	5	6	7	8	9
4	5	6	7	8	9	10
5	6	7	8	9	10	11
6	7	8	9	10	11	12

Each outcome (e.g. throwing a 4 with the first dice and a 2 with the second) has a $\frac{1}{36}$ probability.

However, while there is only a $\frac{1}{36}$ chance of scoring a total of either 2 or 12, there is $\frac{6}{36}$ or $\frac{1}{6}$ chance of scoring a seven.

Independent Events

Independent events are events that have no influence on each other. For example, if a coin is flipped twice then whatever happens the first time does not affect what happens the second time. The two events are independent.

If A and B are two independent events then:

$$\textbf{P(A and B) = P(A)} \times \textbf{P(B)}$$

This important rule **only** applies to independent events. The sample space diagram opposite shows, for example, that **P(HH)** $= \frac{1}{4}$. Notice that this fits the formula for independent events since…

$$\text{P(HH) = P(H) x P(H) = } \frac{1}{2} \times \frac{1}{2} = \frac{1}{4}$$

Probability

Examples

1 A fair dice and a coin are thrown. What is the probability of obtaining Heads and a score greater than 2?

Using H to represent Heads and S to represent a score greater than 2, the events H and S are independent.

$P(H) = \frac{1}{2}$

$P(S) = \frac{4}{6} = \frac{2}{3}$

$P(H \text{ and } S) = P(H) \times P(S) = \frac{1}{2} \times \frac{2}{3} = \frac{2}{6} = \frac{1}{3}$

We can also show this on a sample space diagram.

Score on Dice

		1	2	3	4	5	6
Coin	H	1,H	2,H	3,H	4,H	5,H	6,H
	T	1,T	2,T	3,T	4,T	5,T	6,T

The sample space diagram contains 12 equally likely outcomes. 4 of the outcomes show Heads with a score greater than 2.

$P(H \text{ and } S) = \frac{4}{12} = \frac{1}{3}$ as obtained using the rule for independent events.

2 What is the probability of throwing a 1 or a 2 with a fair dice and picking a red or a green ball from inside a bag that contains 4 black, 5 red and 3 green balls?

Let S represent the event of scoring 1 or 2 with the dice and C represent the event of picking a red or green ball.

$P(S) = \frac{2}{6} = \frac{1}{3}$

$P(C) = \frac{8}{12} = \frac{2}{3}$

The events S and C are independent so...

$P(S \text{ and } C) = P(S) \times P(C) = \frac{1}{3} \times \frac{2}{3} = \frac{2}{9}$

Conditional Probability

If A and B are **not** independent events then the probability that A occurs followed by B is given by:

> **P(A then B) = P(A) x P(B given that A has occurred)**

This is known as **conditional probability**.

Example

A bag contains 3 red socks and 2 blue socks. A sock is selected at random and **not** replaced, then a second sock is selected at random.

What is the probability that both selected socks are blue?

The probability that the first sock is blue is $\frac{2}{5}$

Given that the first sock is blue, only 1 blue sock remains out of 4. The probability that the second sock is also blue must be $\frac{1}{4}$

$P(\text{both blue}) = \frac{2}{5} \times \frac{1}{4} = \frac{2}{20} = \frac{1}{10}$

> N.B. if the first sock was replaced then the events would be independent giving:
> **P(both blue)** $= \frac{2}{5} \times \frac{2}{5} = \frac{4}{25}$

Probability

Tree Diagrams

When dealing with the probability of a sequence of successive events it is often better to use a **tree diagram** in order to simplify the task.

Examples

1 **Flipping Two Fair Coins:** Each coin can give us two possible outcomes, a Head (**H**) or a Tail (**T**).

Calculate the probability of getting...
a) 2 Heads **b)** 2 Tails **c)** a Head and a Tail

We only draw two branches as there are only two different outcomes, i.e. a Head and a Tail.

First Coin   Second Coin

$P(HH) = P(H) \times P(H) = \frac{1}{2} \times \frac{1}{2} = \frac{1}{4}$

$P(HT) = P(H) \times P(T) = \frac{1}{2} \times \frac{1}{2} = \frac{1}{4}$

$P(TH) = P(T) \times P(H) = \frac{1}{2} \times \frac{1}{2} = \frac{1}{4}$

$P(TT) = P(T) \times P(T) = \frac{1}{2} \times \frac{1}{2} = \frac{1}{4}$

Total probability always adds up to 1

a) $P(HH) = \frac{1}{4}$

b) $P(TT) = \frac{1}{4}$

c) $P(HT)$ or $P(TH) = \frac{1}{4} + \frac{1}{4} = \frac{1}{2}$
(these are mutually exclusive outcomes)

2 From Jim's bag, the probability of selecting a red ball is 0.5, a blue ball is 0.3 and a green ball is 0.2. From Sandra's bag, the probability of selecting a red ball is 0.3, a blue ball is 0.3 and a green ball is 0.4. Jim selects a ball at random from his bag, then Sandra selects a ball at random from her bag.

Draw a tree diagram to show all the different outcomes. Then calculate the probability of selecting...
a) 2 Blues
b) 2 Reds or 2 Greens
c) Different colours

This time we draw three branches as there are three different outcomes

Jim's Bag   Sandra's Bag

R	P(RR)	=	0.5	×	0.3	= 0.15
B	P(RB)	=	0.5	×	0.3	= 0.15
G	P(RG)	=	0.5	×	0.4	= 0.20
R	P(BR)	=	0.3	×	0.3	= 0.09
B	P(BB)	=	0.3	×	0.3	= 0.09
G	P(BG)	=	0.3	×	0.4	= 0.12
R	P(GR)	=	0.2	×	0.3	= 0.06
B	P(GB)	=	0.2	×	0.3	= 0.06
G	P(GG)	=	0.2	×	0.4	= 0.08

Total probability always adds up to 1

a) $P(BB) = 0.09$

b) $P(RR$ or $GG) = 0.15 + 0.08 = 0.23$
(these are mutually exclusive outcomes)

c) P(different colours)
= 1 – P(same colours)
= 1 – P(RR or BB or GG)
= 1 – (0.15 + 0.09 + 0.08) = 1 – 0.32
= 0.68

Probability

Tree Diagrams (Cont)

Sometimes the probability of an event occurring depends on the outcome of a previous event. For example, a question may ask you to remove an object at random and then remove a second object at random without replacing the first. When this happens you must remember to adjust your probabilities for the second event.

This is known as conditional probability and a tree diagram, once again, is a useful tool for calculating probabilities based on these events.

Example

Jack's bag contains 10 balls of which 5 are red, 3 are blue and 2 are green. Jack picks a ball at random and, without replacing it, picks another ball at random.

Draw a tree diagram to show all the different possible outcomes. Use the diagram to calculate the probability of Jack picking balls that are…
a) the same colour **b)** different colours.

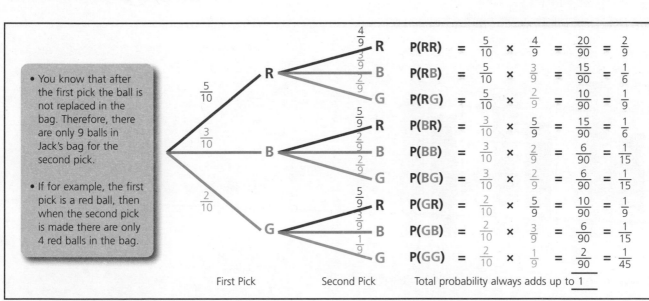

- You know that after the first pick the ball is not replaced in the bag. Therefore, there are only 9 balls in Jack's bag for the second pick.

- If for example, the first pick is a red ball, then when the second pick is made there are only 4 red balls in the bag.

P(RR)	$= \frac{5}{10} \times \frac{4}{9}$	$= \frac{20}{90} = \frac{2}{9}$
P(RB)	$= \frac{5}{10} \times \frac{3}{9}$	$= \frac{15}{90} = \frac{1}{6}$
P(RG)	$= \frac{5}{10} \times \frac{2}{9}$	$= \frac{10}{90} = \frac{1}{9}$
P(BR)	$= \frac{3}{10} \times \frac{5}{9}$	$= \frac{15}{90} = \frac{1}{6}$
P(BB)	$= \frac{3}{10} \times \frac{2}{9}$	$= \frac{6}{90} = \frac{1}{15}$
P(BG)	$= \frac{3}{10} \times \frac{2}{9}$	$= \frac{6}{90} = \frac{1}{15}$
P(GR)	$= \frac{2}{10} \times \frac{5}{9}$	$= \frac{10}{90} = \frac{1}{9}$
P(GB)	$= \frac{2}{10} \times \frac{3}{9}$	$= \frac{6}{90} = \frac{1}{15}$
P(GG)	$= \frac{2}{10} \times \frac{1}{9}$	$= \frac{2}{90} = \frac{1}{45}$

First Pick   Second Pick   Total probability always adds up to 1

a) P(same colour)

= P(RR or BB or GG)

$= \frac{20}{90} + \frac{6}{90} + \frac{2}{90} = \frac{28}{90}$

$= \frac{14}{45}$ (these are mutually exclusive outcomes)

b) P(different colours)

= P(RB or RG or BR or BG or GR or GB)

$= \frac{15}{90} + \frac{10}{90} + \frac{15}{90} + \frac{6}{90} + \frac{10}{90} + \frac{6}{90} = \frac{62}{90}$

$= \frac{31}{45}$ (these are mutually exclusive outcomes)

Alternatively, **P(different colours)**

= 1 – P(same colour)

$= 1 - \frac{14}{45} = \frac{31}{45}$

Probability

Theoretical Probability

Since the chance of a coin landing on Heads is $\frac{1}{2}$, then the number of Heads we should expect in 10 tosses is…

$$\frac{1}{2} \times 10 = 5$$

The most likely number of heads = 5, but this is not certain.

Relative Frequency

A simple experiment was carried out where a coin was tossed 10, 100 and a 1000 times. The graphs below show the number of Heads and Tails obtained. In theory we would expect to always get the same number of Heads and Tails because the probability of each event occurring is $\frac{1}{2}$ or 0.5

Relative Frequency	Coin tossed 10 times	Coin tossed 100 times	Coin tossed 1000 times
	Head = $\frac{4}{10}$ = 0.4	Head = $\frac{44}{100}$ = 0.44	Head = $\frac{480}{1000}$ = 0.48
	Tail = $\frac{6}{10}$ = 0.6	Tail = $\frac{56}{100}$ = 0.56	Tail = $\frac{520}{1000}$ = 0.52

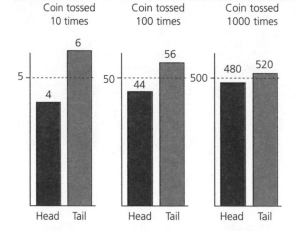

Coin tossed 10 times Coin tossed 100 times Coin tossed 1000 times

The **relative frequency** of obtaining Heads (or Tails) in an experiment is given by:

$$\text{Relative Frequency} = \frac{\text{Number of Heads (or Tails) we get}}{\text{Total number of times the coin was tossed}}$$

If we go back to our experiment, as we increase the number of times the coin is tossed, the relative frequency gets closer and closer to the theoretical probability (red dotted line), e.g. 0.5 for a Head, 0.5 for a Tail.

Theoretical probability relies on equally likely outcomes. If this is not the case, such as when a coin is **biased**, we must use relative frequency to estimate probability.

Importance of Sample Size

As you can see from the data opposite, the bigger the sample, the more reliable it is.

For example, it is quite possible that tossing a coin ten times could produce 2 tails and 8 heads. A larger sample would give a more reliable result.

This has implications in testing for **bias**. For instance, it would be possible to test experimentally the frequency of red and black on a roulette wheel.

If there is time to take a big enough sample then it would be possible to say with some justification that the wheel is not fair, e.g. if 50 000 spins produce 26 750 reds and 23 250 blacks!

Problem Solving and Handling Data

Problem Solving in Statistics

You need to be aware of the problem solving process in statistics and how to use the handling data cycle.

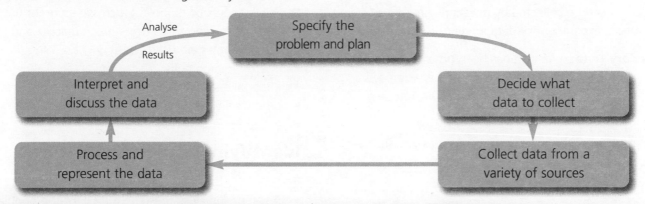

Stage	Examples
Specify the Problem and Plan You need to have a clear understanding of the problem to be solved. You then need to formulate some questions that will provide the necessary information to solve the problem. As the process develops and information is gathered, further lines of enquiry may arise.	• Discuss what better concentration means and how it would be evident in a classroom. • Consider making some observations in lessons. • Which lessons would you observe? • Does the age of pupils make a difference? • Does the ability-set make a difference?
Decide what Data to Collect You need to decide what data you will collect, how it will be collected and how much you will collect (sample size). Think about different types of data, e.g. qualitative and quantitive, discrete and continuous.	• One possibility is to select some pupils in a class and observe them. • The lesson could be divided up into intervals in which these pupils are concentrating or not. • At the end of the lesson each pupil would have a total time. • Consider the use of secondary data.
Collect Data from a Variety of Sources Consider observations, experiments, surveys, and primary and secondary sources. Use suitable data collection techniques, such as the various sampling methods, and give thought to how you will record the data so that it will be easy to work with later.	• A suitable data sheet would be needed to use in the classroom observations. • It may be possible to research the subject on the Internet.
Process and Represent the Data Use relevant statistical measures that summarise the data and consider graphs and charts to represent it.	• You could calculate the mean concentration time for boys and for girls. • The data might be represented using box plots for example.
Interpret and Discuss the Data Consider the data in terms of the original problem and the questions asked. Decide whether the problem has been answered or if further lines of enquiry now need to be followed in a new cycle.	• Use the statistics calculated along with the charts to make comparisons and draw conclusions.
Possible follow-up enquiry	• Do girls / boys do better in single sex lessons / schools?

Collecting Data

Data Handling Definitions

Primary Data: data that has been directly obtained first hand, either by yourself or by someone under your direction. It can be collected by questionnaire, survey, observation, experiment or data logging.

Secondary Data: data that has been obtained independently by an external agency and which may be already stored either in printed or electronic form, e.g. published statistics, data from the Internet.

The Population: the total number of items you are investigating.

The Sample: the limited number of items that you have selected to represent the whole population.

A Random Sample: a sample in that every item of the population has an equal chance of being selected. In practice this means taking great care to spread the 'randomness' over as large an area as possible and to take repeated surveys and work out averages.

A Stratified Sample: a sample that tries to accurately reflect the variation of characteristics within the population, e.g. it reflects the sex distribution, the age distribution, the geographical distribution, the income distribution, etc. It is a small accurate snapshot of the population as a whole. Done properly this method can be very accurate.

Example

Suppose that a survey is to be carried out from a sample of 10% of the employees of a company employing 120 women and 31 men. A basic random sample would consist of 15 employees, but may not have a representative proportion of men and women. A stratified sample would be made up of 12 women and 3 men selected at random.

Reasons for Sampling

Information is a hugely powerful tool in modern society, but clearly it is impossible to survey huge populations. Sampling allows us to look at a cross-section of the population, making the process much quicker and much cheaper. Samples are used widely to…
- inform opinion polls
- undertake market research
- produce T.V. viewing figures
- provide trend analysis.

Identifying Bias in Samples

Consider the following bad examples of sampling:
- A recent survey suggests that 82% of the population prefer Rugby League to Football. The survey was conducted in St Helens.
- A High Street survey reveals that 76% of men aged between 18 and 42 go to the pub at least once a week. The survey was conducted at 11pm.
- A telephone survey suggests that 100% of the population has at least one telephone in their house.

In order to be unbiased, every individual in the population must have an equal chance of being included in the sample. This means taking into account:
- The time of day of the survey
- The age range
- Relative affluence
- The geographical area
- Ethnicity
- Lifestyle

However, you must also remember that the bigger the sample size, the more representative it is likely to be (assuming of course that you have minimised all the other potential areas of bias).

Collecting Data

Collecting Data by Observation

Collecting data by observation can be laborious and time consuming, but for some things it is the best way. For instance, a traffic survey might be done in this way to reveal the volume of traffic using a bridge. You must remember to ask yourself whether the survey is being conducted at an appropriate time and for an appropriate period.

Collecting Data by Experiment

People involved in the Sciences use experiments to gather data to support their hypotheses. The key things to remember are as follows:
- The experiment must be repeated an appropriate number of times.
- Someone else should be able to repeat the experiment in the same way.

Collecting Data by Questionnaire

Questionnaires are skillfully designed forms that are used to conduct surveys of a sample of the population.

Designing a Questionnaire

Good questionnaires have the following things in common:
- They are not too long, i.e. never more than 10 questions, but less if possible.
- They contain questions that are easily understood and do not cause confusion.
- They ask for simple, short answers, e.g. Yes/No, Like/Don't Like or Male/Female
- They avoid vague words like Tall, Old, Fast, Good, etc.
- The questions do not show any bias, e.g. 'Do you prefer watching rugby or hockey?' rather than 'Do you agree that rugby is a more watchable game than hockey?'
- They only contain relevant questions.

Example

Yasmin decides to test the hypothesis that 'Parents would prefer the school holidays to be shorter' by using the following questionnaire.

This tests whether the questionnaire is relevant to this person

The answer may be affected by the size of the family

The answer may turn out to be dependent upon the age of the person's children

This tells us whether or not the person will see a lot of his/her children over the holidays

This avoids asking a 'loaded question', i.e. it avoids bias

QUESTIONNAIRE

1. Do you have children of school age?
   Yes ❑ No ❑

2. How many children do you have?
   1 ❑ 2 ❑ 3 ❑ 4+ ❑

3. To which age group do they belong?
   Under 11 ❑   11–13 ❑
   14–16 ❑   17–18 ❑

4. Are you in full time employment?
   Yes ❑ No ❑

5. Do you think the school holidays are…
   Too Short? ❑
   Too Long? ❑
   Just Right? ❑

From the answers, Yasmin could…
1. reject any responses from people who aren't parents
2. analyse the data to see if family size, age range and employment status affect the answers
3. come up with a pretty good answer to her original hypothesis.

Sorting Data

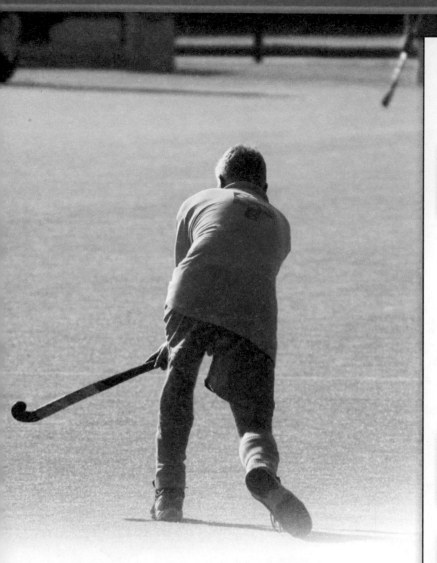

Discrete and Continuous Data

Data comes in many different forms. To make sense of the data it is often sorted and collated. There are two different types of data that you can record for sorting and collating.

Discrete data is data that can only have certain values. For example, the number of goals a football team can score in a match is 0, 1, 2, 3, 4, etc. They cannot have a score in between, like 0.5, 1.6, 2.2, etc.

Continuous data is data that can have any value. It tends to be obtained by reading measuring instruments. The accuracy of the data is dependent on the precision of the equipment.

Tally Charts and Frequency Tables
Very often the best way to sort and collate discrete or continuous data is to draw a tally chart and a frequency table.

Example
The results below show the games involving Germany, in Round 1 through to the semi-finals of a Hockey World Cup Tournament.

Germany 4 Costa Rica 2	Germany 2 Sweden 0
Germany 1 Poland 0	Germany 4 Argentina 2
Germany 0 Brazil 3	Germany 0 Italy 2

Sort the number of goals scored per game by each team by drawing a tally chart and a frequency table.

Since the range of data here is narrow (e.g. from 0 to 4 goals scored) each value can be included individually in the tally chart and frequency table. As you complete the tally column always tick off each number as you go along. This makes sure that you don't include the same number twice or miss any out.

Germany 4 Costa Rica 2	Germany 2 Sweden 0
Germany 1 Poland 0	Germany 4 Argentina 2
Germany 0 Brazil 3	Germany 0 Italy 2

Number of goals scored	Tally	Frequency of that no. of goals being scored by a team
0	IIII	4
1	I	1
2	IIII	4
3	I	1
4	II	2
		Total = 12

The numbers in the frequency column are simply the number of tallies. Remember to add them up, as this total is equal to the total number of pieces of data (not, in this example, the total number of goals scored!).

N.B. The data in this example is discrete, however, the same process would apply for continuous data.

Sorting Data

Using Class Intervals

Sometimes, data is so widespread that it is impractical to include each value in the tally chart and frequency table individually. When this happens, the data is sorted into groups called **class intervals**, where each class interval represents a range of values.

Example

The newspaper cutting shows the recorded temperatures in °C for various places both at home and abroad. Sort the recorded temperatures, by drawing a tally chart and a frequency table.

Temperatures home and abroad

Amsterdam	19	Cairo	34	Majorca	27	New York	32
Athens	33	Cardiff	16	Manchester	12	Newcastle	13
Barbados	29	Dublin	15	Miami	26	Paris	20
Barcelona	26	Jersey	20	Milan	28	Peking	33
Berlin	23	London	21	Montreal	22	Prague	26
Bermuda	28	Madrid	33	Moscow	15	Rhodes	28

There is a wide range of data shown above, i.e. from 12°C to 34°C. Out of practicality, the temperature values are arranged in groups of five in our tally chart and frequency table.

The class interval $10 \leqslant T < 15$ would include any temperature reading equal to or greater than 10°C and less than 15°C (a temperature reading of 15°C is included in the next class interval) and so on.

Remember to total the numbers in the frequency column to make sure they add up to the total number of locations (pieces of data).

Recorded Temperatures, T(°C)	Tally	Frequency of Temperatures Falling Within that Range
$10 \leqslant T < 15$	II	2
$15 \leqslant T < 20$	IIII	4
$20 \leqslant T < 25$	IIII	5
$25 \leqslant T < 30$	IIII III	8
$30 \leqslant T < 35$	IIII	5
		Total = 24

N.B. The data in this example is continuous, however, the same process would apply for discrete data.

Two Important Points

- The format of class intervals can vary. The following class intervals could have been used to give the same results for the data above: 10–14, 15–19, 20–24, etc.
- The range of each class interval depends on the total range of the data. If the total range of the data is large and the range of each class interval is small, then your frequency table would have a lot of rows. Aim to have no more than 10 rows in your table.

Sorting Data

Stem and Leaf Diagrams

A stem and leaf diagram sorts data into groups.

One advantage of these diagrams over frequency tables is that they enable you to get more of a feel for the 'shape' of the distribution.

Example

The following data shows the length of time (in minutes) it took 30 pupils to complete a test, arranged in ascending order:

8, 8, 9, 15, 15, 16, 16, 17, 18, 18, 20, 21, 21, 22, 23, 26, 27, 27, 28, 28, 29, 33, 34, 34, 35, 39, 39, 42, 48, 49

This data can be represented using a stem and leaf diagram by taking the tens to form the 'stem' of the diagram and the units to form the 'leaves'.

Key: **1** | **5** means **15**

0	8 8 9
1	5 5 6 6 7 8 8
2	0 1 1 2 3 6 7 7 8 8 9
3	3 4 4 5 9 9
4	2 8 9

Stem   Leaves

The end product is similar to a frequency table. However, besides allowing you to visualise the 'shape' of the data, it can be used to identify the modal class, i.e. the 20–29 group and the median, i.e. 24.5 (between the 15th and 16th pieces of data as there are 30 values, see page 105).

Two-Way Tables

Two-way tables simply show two sets of information, one vertically and the other horizontally. Information organised in this way can actually result in you gaining more information than you started with.

Example

'In a survey, 200 Year 7 and 8 pupils were asked if they preferred maths or science. 73 out of 110 Year 7 pupils preferred maths, and in total 82 pupils preferred science.' This could lead to the table below:

	Year 7	Year 8	Total
Science			82
Maths	73		
Total	110		200

This in turn can be used to work out the missing data:

	Year 7	Year 8	Total
Science	37	45	82
Maths	73	45	118
Total	110	90	200

Notice that in the original table there was no data for Year 8 … now it is all there!

Various Types of Table

Tables can be arranged in many different ways to suit the purpose for which they are intended. Remember, the idea is to make the information as accessible as possible, so you have got to give a bit of thought as to how you want to present it.

Averages and Spread

Mean, Median, Mode and Range

The **mean** is given by the following formula:

$$\text{Mean} = \frac{\textbf{Sum of the values}}{\textbf{Number of values}}$$

The **median** is the middle value once the data has been put in order of size. For an even number of values, add the middle pair and divide by 2 to find the median.

The **mode** is the most common data value, i.e. the one that occurs with the greatest frequency.

The **range** measures the **spread** of the data and is the difference between the smallest and largest data values.

Mean, Median, Mode and Range from a Frequency Table

Here is the frequency table for the number of goals scored in games involving Germany, from Round 1 through to the semi-finals of a Hockey World Cup Tournament. The data in this frequency table is discrete.

Number of Goals Scored (x)	Frequency (f)	Frequency × no. of Goals Scored (fx)
0	4	4 × 0 = 0
1	1	1 × 1 = 1
2	4	4 × 2 = 8
3	1	1 × 3 = 3
4	2	2 × 4 = 8
	Total = 12	Total = 20

To calculate the **mean** we need to add another column (in green) to our frequency table to calculate the total number of goals scored.

$$\text{Mean} = \frac{\text{Total number of goals scored (f}x)}{\text{Total frequency}}$$
$$= \frac{20}{12} = 1.\dot{6} \textbf{ goals (per team per game)}$$

Mode = 0 and 2 goals
(because these occur more times than any of the others).

Since we have 12 pieces of data, the **median** number of goals is halfway between the 6th and 7th piece of data.

4 teams scored	1 team scored	4 teams scored	1 team scored	2 teams scored
0̸ 0̸ 0̸ 0̸	1̸	②②2̸2̸	3̸	4̸ 4̸

$$\text{Median} = \frac{2+2}{2} = \textbf{2 goals}$$

Range = 4 goals – 0 goals = **4 goals**

Mean, Median, Mode and Range from a Frequency Table of Grouped Data

Here is the frequency table for the recorded temperatures for various locations at home and abroad. The data in this frequency table is continuous.

Recorded Temp., T (°C)	Frequency (f)	Mid-Temp. Values (x)	Frequency × Mid-Temp. Values (fx)
10 ⩽ T < 15	2	12.5	2 × 12.5 = 25
15 ⩽ T < 20	4	17.5	4 × 17.5 = 70
20 ⩽ T < 25	5	22.5	5 × 22.5 = 112.5
25 ⩽ T < 30	8	27.5	8 × 27.5 = 220
30 ⩽ T < 35	5	32.5	5 × 32.5 = 162.5
	Total = 24		Total = 590

These are class intervals

These are halfway values for our class intervals

Estimated Mean

With grouped data, the individual values are unknown. Therefore, we have to use 'mid-temperature value' to provide an **estimate** of the mean. To calculate the mean this time we need to add two further columns (in green) to our frequency table.

$$\text{Mean} = \frac{\text{Total of Recorded Temperatures (f}x)}{\text{Total Frequency}}$$
$$= \frac{590}{24}$$
$$= \textbf{24.6°C}$$

Mode

We don't get an exact mode but we are able to determine which class interval or group is the **Modal Class**. Modal Class is **25°C ⩽ T < 30°C** since this class interval has the highest frequency (i.e. it occurs the most number of times).

Median

With continuous data we don't get an exact value for the median, but we are able to determine which class interval or group it is in. The above table has 24 pieces of data and so the median is halfway between the 12th and 13th piece of data. Using the frequency column, the median is in the **25°C ⩽ T < 30°C** class interval.

Displaying Data

Displaying Data from a Table

The best way of displaying data that has been sorted into a frequency table is to draw a graph.

Here is the frequency table for the number of goals scored in games involving Germany in Round 1 through to the semi-finals of a Hockey World Cup Tournament.

No. of goals scored	0	1	2	3	4
Frequency	4	1	4	1	2

A Vertical Line Graph
This graph is very similar to bar graphs, except that lines are drawn instead of bars. Make sure that the height of each line is equal to the correct frequency.

A Line Graph
This is not always the most suitable way to display discrete data, as the lines joining the points have no meaning!

Dual and Composite Bar Charts
Data from two or more groups may be shown on a single chart. A **dual** bar chart shows the bars side by side and a **composite** bar chart combines the responses in a single bar. A key is needed to explain what each part of the chart represents.

Displaying Grouped Data

Data that has been grouped together and sorted, using class intervals, in a frequency table can also be displayed by drawing a graph.

Here is the frequency table for the recorded temperatures for various locations at home and abroad.

Recorded Temperatures T(°C)	Frequency
$10 \leqslant T < 15$	2
$15 \leqslant T < 20$	4
$20 \leqslant T < 25$	5
$25 \leqslant T < 30$	8
$30 \leqslant T < 35$	5

This data can be displayed in various ways:

A frequency diagram is very much like a bar graph, but because the data is grouped the bars do not have a gap between them, i.e. they must be continuous.

A frequency polygon is created by marking the middle of the top of each bar in the frequency diagram with a cross and then joining up these crosses with straight lines.

You may be asked to draw a frequency polygon directly from the frequency table. You must remember to plot the crosses at the correct frequency exactly over the middle of the class intervals, e.g. for **$10 \leqslant T < 15$**, plot the cross above 12.5.

Displaying Data

Histograms

Frequency graphs for grouped continuous data where the **area** of each column represents the **frequency** of that **class interval** are called **histograms**.

Example
The frequency table below shows the distribution of the ages of the people in a supermarket at a particular time. Draw a histogram to illustrate this data.

Before we can draw our histogram we need to add a further column (in green) to our table for **frequency density**. It can easily be calculated using:

$$\text{Frequency Density} = \frac{\text{Frequency of class interval}}{\text{Width of class interval}}$$

Age, A (Years)	Frequency	Frequency Density
$0 \leqslant A < 10$	10	1
$10 \leqslant A < 20$	20	2
$20 \leqslant A < 30$	60	6
$30 \leqslant A < 40$	50	5
$40 \leqslant A < 60$	60	3
$60 \leqslant A < 100$	20	0.5

We can now draw the histogram.

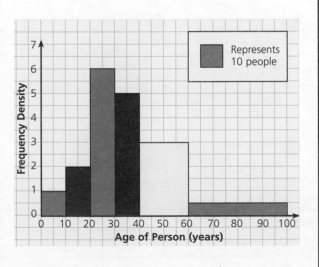

Scatter Diagrams

A scatter diagram is a graph that has two sets of data plotted on it at the same time. When plotted, the points may show a certain trend or correlation. A **correlation** is defined as the 'strength of relationship between two variables'.

Positive Correlation
As one increases, the other also increases, e.g. number of ice creams sold and daytime temperature.

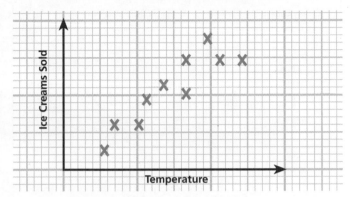

Negative Correlation
As one increases, the other decreases or vice versa, e.g. amount of petrol left in tank and distance travelled by car.

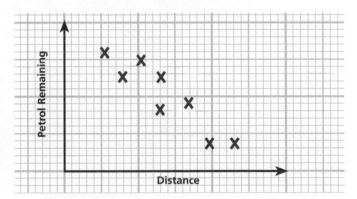

Zero Correlation
No obvious trend between the two, e.g. length of hair and height. Remember that zero correlation does not necessarily imply 'no relationship' but merely 'no linear relationship'.

Displaying Data

Using a Line of Best Fit on a Scatter Diagram

A line of best fit can be used to estimate unknown values. This method is unreliable for providing estimates outside the range of values plotted.

Example

The diagram shows a strong positive correlation between some maths and science marks.

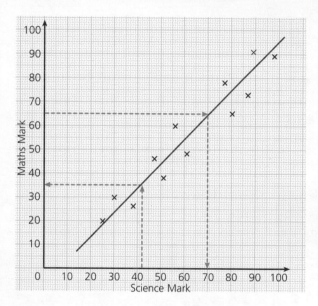

The line of best fit (red line) may be used to estimate the score on one test based on the score in the other. The green dotted line shows that a pupil who scored 65 in maths, but missed the science test, could be given an estimated mark of 70 in science.

Similarly, the blue line shows that a pupil who scored 42 in science could be given an estimated mark of 35 in maths.

A* Tip

Drawing pie charts is usually worth around 4 marks; make sure your angles add up to 360°, and draw accurately because you are only allowed a 2° tolerance.

Pie Charts

In a pie chart, the frequency for each class must be shown as a proportion. To draw a pie chart, we need to calculate the angle of the sector for each category.

Example

Favourite Sport	Frequency (no. of pupils)
Football	7
Tennis	3
Hockey	8
	Total = 18

Favourite Sport	Proportion of Pupils	Angle to be Drawn
Football	$\frac{7}{18}$	$\frac{7}{18} \times 360° = 140°$
Tennis	$\frac{3}{18}$	$\frac{3}{18} \times 360° = 60°$
Hockey	$\frac{8}{18}$	$\frac{8}{18} \times 360° = 160°$
		Total = 360°

Number who like hockey

Total number of pupils

1. Pick a starting point and draw a radius

2. Measure and mark 140° for football

3. Measure and mark 60° for tennis

4. Check that the remainder (for hockey) is 160°

5. The completed pie chart will now look like this

Cumulative Frequency Diagrams

A cumulative frequency diagram usually produces an 's' shaped curve. It can be used to analyse the distribution of the data.

Example

The grouped frequency table alongside shows the time taken by 80 girls to travel to school on one particular day (to the nearest minute).

The cumulative frequency is the total frequency of that class interval, plus all the class intervals that precede it.

All points are plotted at the upper boundary of each class interval, e.g. (10,5), (20,14) etc.

Time Taken, T (minutes)	Frequency (i.e. no. of girls)	Cumulative Frequency
$0 < T \leqslant 10$	5	5
$10 < T \leqslant 20$	9	(9 + 5 =) 14
$20 < T \leqslant 30$	16	(16 + 14 =) 30
$30 < T \leqslant 40$	29	(29 + 30 =) 59
$40 < T \leqslant 50$	15	(15 + 59 =) 74
$50 < T \leqslant 60$	6	(6 + 74 =) 80

Once we have drawn the cumulative frequency diagram there are two ways we can compare the distribution of the data:

Median

The median is the middle value of our data. The median is obtained by drawing a line across (➥) from half way up the cumulative frequency axis to the curve and then down (▼) to give its value. (In our graph this is at 40, i.e. $\frac{1}{2}$ of 80).

Interquartile Range

> **Interquartile range = Upper quartile – Lower quartile**

This gives us a measure of the spread of the data about the median. Two values are needed.

a) A line is drawn across (➥) from three quarters of the way up the cumulative frequency axis and then down (▼). This value is called the **upper quartile**. (In our graph this is at 60, i.e. $\frac{3}{4}$ of 80).

b) A line is drawn across (➥) from one quarter of the way up the cumulative frequency axis and then down (▼). This value is called the **lower quartile**. (In our graph this is at 20, i.e. $\frac{1}{4}$ of 80).

If we compare line ① at the bottom of our frequency curve with ②, we can see that a **box and whisker diagram** (or box plot) presents this more visually by differentiating between the interquartile range and the full range.

The method of displaying the median, quartiles and range is useful for comparing cumulative frequency graphs (as they all tend to have similar shapes).

This box and whisker diagram shows a reasonably symmetrical distribution but diagram **a)** below shows a positively skewed distribution with the median closer to the lower quartile while diagram **b)** shows a negative skew with the median closer to the upper quartile

Formulae Sheet

Area of a trapezium $= \frac{1}{2}(a + b)h$

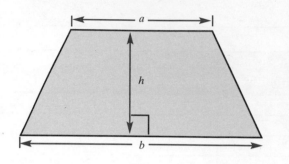

Volume of a prism = area of cross section x length

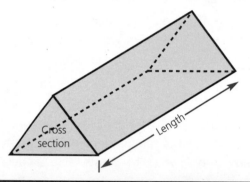

Volume of a sphere $= \frac{4}{3}\pi r^3$

Surface area of a sphere $= 4\pi r^2$

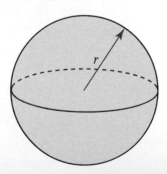

Volume of a cone $= \frac{1}{3}\pi r^2 h$

Curved surface area of a cone $= \pi r l$

In any triangle ABC

Area of triangle $= \frac{1}{2}ab\sin C$

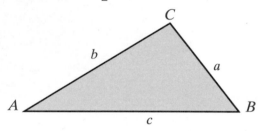

Sine rule: $\dfrac{a}{\sin A} = \dfrac{b}{\sin B} = \dfrac{c}{\sin C}$

Cosine rule: $a^2 = b^2 + c^2 - 2bc\cos A$

The Quadratic Equation

The solutions of $ax^2 + bx + c = 0$, where $a \neq 0$, are given by

$$x = \frac{-b \pm \sqrt{b^2 - 4ac}}{2a}$$

Exam Tips

When you have a 'show that' question, you already know the answer. So, you must carefully show all the steps required to get there – do not just make assumptions.

In many questions it is wise to show each step of your working out, as you can earn method marks even if the final answer is wrong.

Become familiar with the basic shapes of standard graphs, so that you know roughly what to expect – positive/negative quadratics, cubics, parabolas, hyperbolas, sin/cos/tan curves, cumulative frequencies.

Sketches and diagrams can give you a good idea of how to tackle a problem before you start it, especially with angles, bearings, trigonometry, etc.

Make sure you answer the question. For example:
- If a graphical solution is asked for, don't use algebra and vice versa.
- If told to use the equation, don't do trial and error/trial and improvement.

Make sure you check your answers. For example:
- After factorising, multiply out and vice versa.
- After solving equations, substitute back into the original.

When asked to find angle XYZ or $\angle$ XYZ or $X\hat{Y}Z$, find the middle letter angle, i.e. Y

If a question does not specify the number of decimal places or significant figures that the answer should be in, give your answer to the same number of decimal places / significant figures that occurs in the question.

When comparing graphs, comment on the overall trends, any common values/elements, and any 'odd' values.

Maths requires lots of regular practice, rather than just reading through things.

Get to know your calculator and all its functions thoroughly.

The amount of marks allocated to a question is a clue as to how much working is expected.

Do not lose marks through untidy handwriting. Presentation is important – an examiner has to be able to decipher what you have written in order to award you marks.

When calculating surds, don't use a calculator; the exact answer is not required – it's a test of your ability to manipulate the items.

When asked to 'explain' in angle questions, always refer to angle properties and try to use the correct terms: adjacent, alternate, corresponding, etc.

Index